With love to Eve,
and many thanks for
your encouragement!

Keith

October, 2009

Rumoledew

TELLING TALES IN A NORFOLK VILLAGE

Rumoledew

TELLING TALES IN A NORFOLK VILLAGE

Keith Skipper

HALSGROVE

First published in Great Britain in 2009

Copyright © Keith Skipper 2009

British Library Cataloguing-in-Publication Data
A CIP record for this title is available from the British Library

ISBN 978 1 84114 969 1

HALSGROVE
Halsgrove House,
Ryelands Industrial Estate,
Bagley Road, Wellington, Somerset TA21 9PZ
Tel: 01823 653777   Fax: 01823 216796
email: sales@halsgrove.com

Part of the Halsgrove group of companies
Information on all Halsgrove titles is available at: www.halsgrove.com

Printed and bound by The Cromwell Press Group, Wiltshire

CONTENTS

Introduction 7

1 An Average Parish 9

2 Oldest Resident 17

3 The Name Game 21

4 First with News 23

5 Special Agent 29

6 A Bright Future 33

7 Keeping Peace 41

8 Drama Queen 47

9 Mine Host 51

10 Coming Home 55

11 Local Flavour 59

12 Lifting the Lid 65

13 Sound of Silence 69

14 Close to Nature 73

15 Young Outlook 77

16 Mucking In 81

17 Promised Land 85

18 Farmyard Fresh 89

19 Faith Restored 93

20 Prodigal Daughter .97

21 Cleaning Up Roots 103

22 The Last Word 113

OUR VILLAGE
By Natalie Higgs, age 14

A shop, a pub, a church, a school
A parish stage to play the fool
In village hall at festive time
When locals fall about in rhyme
Fields may call to only few
But still we feel the morning dew
Count those furrows from the past
Make the golden sunsets last
Keep the rustic flavour strong
Ask the pigs to share their pong
Let the roosters crow at dawn
Sound the church bells Sunday morn
Chat and smile and cogitate
And tell commuters: "Don't be late,
Rumoledew will take you back
When you come home to hit the sack"

The Muckspreader, 2009

INTRODUCTION

Born and raised in a Norfolk village of similar size and flavour, I can identify closely with the lives and times of many Rumoledew residents.

Perhaps there's more of a mixture of people and aspirations on parade than in my formative years just after the last war but essential rural values remain unchanged. Indeed, a need for roots and permanence is lodged deeply in most of us.

The village still symbolises a place from which strength and reassurance can be drawn, where the past is treated with genuine respect, neighbourliness is a way of life and where no-one needs to be a stranger.

I have maintained close links with the good old parish pump throughout a lengthy working career as journalist, broadcaster, author and entertainer in my native county.

Newcomers now play important roles in priming the pump-some even get the chance to work the handle-and the following Rumoledew reflections include plenty of scope for that fresh brand of togetherness.

Yes, suspicions persist that some of the more brazen inter-lopers are hell-bent on pushing through an agenda fashioned out of ugly urban excesses supposedly left behind.

And allegations still arise that some of the less flexible locals are determined to hold back any inkling of an idea likely to challenge the way things have always been done. So there!

Still, a lively exchange of opinions must be preferred to another deadly dose of apathy. I know from countless visits to village events how the combined influences of old and new can tease out the right kind of community spirit.

I hear fond echoes of a quieter, slower more intimate way of village life in the following pages. I also detect a healthy determination to take on the inevitable challenge of change, much of it aimed at the future of family foundations in the countryside.

For Norfolk to stay relatively true to its "dew diffrunt" mantra, nothing short of a social revolution will suffice when it comes to provision of affordable homes, especially for young folk who want to stay close to rural roots.

Perhaps parish councils will be allowed more power to help turn lip-service into overdue action.

Perhaps Rumoledew can then join an exciting modern chorus in favour of those old-fashioned virtues, continuity and self-sufficiency.

Keith Skipper
Cromer, 2009

1
AN AVERAGE PARISH

Rumoledew is nowhere in Norfolk. Rumoledew is every-where in Norfolk...

A village of just under 500 souls, many of them clearly bound for the fires of eternal damnation according to at least two veteran residents, it likes to think it has clung on to rural roots despite a fair bit of physical expansion and tradition-testing in recent years.

The primary school, under constant threat in the 1980s, happily remains open with a growing register and reputation to attract more young families into the community. There's a free-house pub, The Four Ferrets, a combined shop and post office defying all the odds, a garage near the cross-roads and a pallet-making business near the old railway station.

Rumoledew Methodist Chapel closed 20 years ago and became a private house but the parish church dedicated to St Bartholomew is well supported as the main one in group of six looked after by an energetic young parson raised and trained in Birmingham.

There's a clutch of old-established family farms on and around the edges of the parish although numbers employed on the land have dwindled to a handful.

Most Rumoledew workers commute by car to office in town and city, including a few who stay in London throughout the week and creep back to darkest Norfolk on Friday evenings to recharge batteries, practice quaint local dialect phrases in The Four Ferrets and ask where they have to get their passports stamped.

This "Bolt-hole Brigade", as christened by the pub landlord, albeit safely behind their backs, readily admit they need a rustic retreat after piling up hours and bonuses in the capital. "Best of both worlds" is the cry bound to antagonise some who've only lived in one.

Still, a fairly healthy spirit runs through this lively settlement with several newcomers – folk who have lived here for less than a decade – joining local clubs and organisations. A new estate, The Pastures, introduced a contingent of the well-heeled, mostly retired, to help run and support activities at the modern village hall.

Occasional outbreaks of "Them versus Us" can flare into nasty warfare, especially at parish council meetings when virtually every radical idea proposed by newcomers is opposed by natives as a matter of course. For all that, a united front can emerge in the face of gross insensitivity on the part of district and county councils. Developers have been known to eye green acres around Rumoledew with interest bordering on the passionate.

One or two family feuds stretch back to pre-war days – that's the first world war – although an increasingly cosmopolitan population gives most arguments a wider span. Rumours started in the shop get embellished at the pub and then dispelled when firm evidence is demanded at an official parish get-together. There's some reverence for authority.

The village is distant enough from big centres of population and the coastal holiday beat to be described as a country community. It has few qualms when it comes to feeding misconceptions among urban dwellers about roses round the door, donkeys on the green, stocks behind the pub and straw-chewing yokels wearing smocks and manic smiles as they roll dumplings along the disused railway line on bank holidays.

The parish magazine, The Muckspreader, compiled and edited by retired schoolteacher Alec Paine, actively encourages hefty swigs of cheerful self-denigration. "Homely blood-letting" includes a Confessional Box where well-known village characters answer awkward questions about certain perceived prejudices and doubtful traits.

A former vice-chairman of the parish council, renowned for his charisma bypass and lack of humour, provided a series of dead straight answers. His reputation changed overnight. Readers thought he was trying to be funny as no-one could possibly take those responses seriously. The Confessional Box bought him sudden salvation and cheery greetings after years of snide remarks and stifled titters. "He could only see a joke by appointment" had been an early verdict on his local government career.

It worked in the other direction, however, for a notoriously snobbish woman, pillar of the Women's Institute and church flower -arranging committee. Replying to a question regarding the rights and wrongs of pre-marital sex, she attempted to smother automatic abhorrence of the subject by offering "indifferent". She blushed several shades of scarlet when

DOCTOR'S NOTE

The parish council has been informed of the proposed change of name by Dr E. G. Osborne regarding his residence in Back Lane.

Our much-loved family practitioner retires towards the end of the year (see our next edition for full details) but will continue to live in the village.

He has asked for permission to turn The Cedars, his home since 1928, into Bedside Manor.

The Muckspreader, 1960

TALKING SHOP

Gladys Spring has asked us to extend her heartfelt thanks to all customers and friends who contributed to her farewell party at the village hall.

Miss Spring, who ran the shop and post office for nearly 40 years, was presented with a cheque and bouquet of flowers after several speeches full of praise for her long-standing role in the local community.

Mr Hugh Gaskin, chairman of the parish council, described her as "the easiest person to collect for in the village" and wished her many happy years of retirement. He urged strong support for Enid Trett, her successor behind the counter.

Pupils from the village primary school performed a song written specially for the retirement occasion by headmistress Miss Purton – Spring Chorus.

The Muckspreader, 1982

someone inquired loudly at a packed local function whether she had meant that as one word or two.

Alec Paine is regarded as something of a village father figure, often approached confidentially for advice on all manner of issues. His gentle manner, tactful stance and wide knowledge of local affairs offer a comfort zone for worried characters.

At his behest, those who offer village views in the following pages are also encouraged to own up to something that may surprise, even shock, their fellow residents.

"A few secrets brought into the open adds real spice to a social exercise like this" he says. "It's not designed to embarrass but more to show other communities of comparable size and nature how making a clean breast of certain issues, many of them riddled with rumour and confusion, can do a power of good.

"Well, that's my excuse – and I'm sticking to it!"

There are dark corners in Rumoledew as well as the copse popular with courting couples just past the old railway station and the area known as Doodlebug Corner beyond the allotments.

Elijah Barker's sudden disappearance in 1957 with his housekeeper and pub darts club funds – none were ever seen again – still gives rise to idle speculation among older patrons in The Four Ferrets on a quiet night.

Long-serving judges of rural reputations say they can understand the attraction of the money, over £50 in the kitty, but simply cannot fathom Elijah's apparent willingness to share it with sharp-nosed Carrie Cox. Neat lines along "cash-and-Carrie" themes persist.

The baffling case of Amy Palmer's disappearing dogs during the bitter winter of 1963 – she lost four prize Airedale Terriers

GOLDEN MILESTONE FOR INSTITUTE

Congratulations to Rumoledew and District Women's Institute on reaching a golden milestone.

Members enjoyed cuttings from a "memory tree" at a special meeting in the village hall to mark the institute's 50th birthday. Two founder-members, Ethel Maitland and Amy Robinson were invited to cut the birthday cake and they regaled the company with stories from the early years.

Memories from the tree included a press report of the inaugural meeting in April, 1930, when president Lorna Gaskin urged local women "of all ages and all types" to support this new organisation.

Another newspaper cutting highlighted a talk given in 1949 by Canon Hugh Elfleet, an expert on musical instruments. "WI spellbound by serpent" ran the headline.

Entertainment for the 50th anniversary celebrations was provided by The Rumoledew Revellers, five Institute members with sketches and their own versions of popular songs.

A vote of thanks was given by Nell Boldero and birthday posies were presented to Amy Robinson and Myra Hooper.

Lorna Gaskin, president of Rumoledew and District WI when it was founded in 1930.

The Muckspreader, 1980

from her back garden kennels inside a week – remains a bone of contention between her family and several show rivals in a nearby parish.

In more recent times Rumoledew affairs have been dominated by rows over planning applications, street lighting, noisy youngsters, allotment lettings, thoughtless parking, dog-fouling, speeding traffic and an alleged clique of newcomers dominating the village drama group and claiming all the best roles.

On the whole, though, Rumoledew follows gently predictable patterns of Norfolk parish existence as a fairly new millennium teases residents old and new into accepting that a simple life in the sticks remains infinitely preferable to urban clamour, clutter and chaos.

Judge for yourself as Rumoledew chroniclers, all volunteers, paint pictures in words. They are helped by colourful extracts from The Muckspreader celebrating various village milestones and characters over the years.

There are bold strokes, nifty touches, surprise patches, reckless daubs, inevitable smudges.

Even so, it's a shared canvas worked on with enthusiasm and no little pride, worthy of a place in any Norfolk gallery.

MISSING POINT

It is evident that not all Rumoledew residents got the point when we changed to decimal currency earlier this year.

One regular user of the village shop and post office was heard to declare:"They should have waited until all the old people died."

The Muckspreader, 1971

CONFESSIONAL BOX
Tickler Haynes

Welcome to another edition of Confessional Box, where well-known village personalities are asked to give straight answers to straight questions.

Our latest "victim" is Percy Haynes, known to all as Tickler, as he prepares to celebrate his 80th birthday. We begin with the obvious question:

Why are you called Tickler? – That goes back to schooldays and what we got up to on the way home. My brother Claude used to say if you make the gals laugh you were halfway there...

Did it work? – Not really, I couldn't work out the other half.

What are your main qualities? – I still get up before the streets are aired and go to bed before I'm bored. I never speak ill of anyone unless they upset me. I pay all bills on time.

Do you have any big faults? – Dark shag tobacco. My old pipe can stink the place out and it makes me spit on the fire. And I have been known to cough and splutter while someone is talking. That's why I say "Pardon?" a lot.

What's your biggest regret? - Listening to old boys on the farm who said smoking was good for you. I'm too set in my ways to pack up now. But it's my only vice.

Your proudest achievement? - Arriving in this world a few days before Walter Grimes. That meant I could pull rank on him at school, on the farm and down the Evergreens Club.

What, if anything, would you change about the village? – I'd have extra allotments to encourage people to grow more of their own grub like families used to. And I'd fine anyone refusing to give the seal of the day with a smile when greeted cordially in the street.

How would you like to be remembered – As someone who meant what he said and said what he meant.

Happy birthday, Tickler!

The Muckspreader, 1997

2
OLDEST RESIDENT

Oldest resident, Walter Grimes, was born in the village just over 91 years ago a few yards from his present home, a bungalow in the grounds of Holly Farm. He worked on that farm for over 50 years. Naturally, he regrets the steep decline in local numbers connected directly with the land.

I only become oldest resident last year when Tickler Haynes handed in his dinner pail.

He stayed a few days ahead o' me from when we was at school and worked on the farm together until our joint 90th birthday party at the Evergreens Club. Rare nice do. Tickler insisted on having' first huff at all them candles. He ran out o' breath altogether six hours later.

I took over the Rumoledew crown and I hope to have it on my skull for a fair while yet.

Mind you, I do remember what several old boys tell me when they come home from the trenches – live each day as if that is your last – and one day you'll be right!

There's a bit of respect to go with honour of being oldest resident. I never have to wait to draw my pension at the post office and I always get served first at big local functions. Reckon they think I might pop my clogs before the cheese and biscuits.

Then there's all them young reporters banging on my door when suffin important happen in the village. Good job they can't contradict me when I go back a few year, though some of what I tell 'em might be true.

Rumoledew today? Too many strangers for my liking, but I still enjoy living here on my own midden rather than being cooped up in some old people's home. My niece Linda and her husband Mick live close by, so they drop in most days to see if I'm still jamming about. I have my garden and there's still a few places to take a nice walk and hear the crops growing.

Noise and traffic, they're biggest differences from when I was a boy. And if they can craze you round here, goodness only knows how they survive in them towns and cities. Sorft and deaf the lot of 'em, I reckon. I never wed, so I do know what peace and quiet sound like.

Seem to me horse power was a sight safer and quieter when the horses had it. The way some of them young clients roar them motor cars up and down our streets make me wonder if they hent got a death wish.

"Good horses, good farm" was a saying that rang true when I first went to work on the land. The men looked after the horses as well as worked with them and took great pride in their appearance. There was real competition among the farms... braid and ribbons, shiny coats and harness in perfect condition. Those days were long and hard, specially during the corn harvest when teams of horses were changed halfway through the day to give them a rest.

We had a blacksmith, harness-maker and wheelwright in the village before the last war, so that shows just how big a part horses played in local life. You could depend on 'em in all weathers and in all seasons.

They say the old characters are disappearing fast from village life. Well, they do have a habit of dying and taking a rare lot of experience and know-how with 'em. But they wuz doing that when I was a lad on the farm. Least nowadays they can record your memories and put 'em in a museum if they think you might be a vital link with a world disappearing over the headlands. As Tickler used to say, we are tomorrow's past.

Of course, all this don't mean you can't be ambitious just because you're ancient and able to whistle while you clean your teeth. I have three main targets left – to see Norwich City win the FA Cup, to reach my century so I can show off when I meet Tickler again and to be shot dead by a jealous husband. Wonder which one will come first...

Now for this here "dark secret" we're supposed to own up to. Don't think that'll do any harm after all this time. That go back to when I mooched about with Aniseed Boulton and Ginger Cason in the summer holidays of 1929.

We see old Barney Wheeler eating his fourses up against the hedge at bottom o' Buscall's Meadow on Primrose Farm. We know he always have a good clear-out after his grub, so we decide to play a little trick. Ginger tied a spade to a long pole and pushed that gently through the hedge while Barney was busy with his overalls down.

'Cors, when he turn round to check what he'd done, there was noffin there. Poor old boy couldn't make that out and he went a funny colour and started shouting.

We got the wind up and Ginger tried to push the evidence back through the hedge. Barney was out of there in a hurry, charging towards his sister's cottage at back of the farm. God know what he told her, or the doctor, but the old boy was never quite the same after that.

That was only meant to be a bit of squit, but that told us to be a bit more careful when that come to playing tricks on people.

Little beggars today, some of them have a nasty streak, specially when they get some drink into them. We could never afford very much when we was young and had to make our own entertainment. There was plenty to do in the country and we thought noffin of spending a whole day rambling across the fields with bread and cheese and a bottle of cold tea.

I have never lived in town or city but I know that wouldn't suit me. Fresh air and space have kept me going up and down the Rumoledew hidlands since end of the first world war. That may not be the perfect village ... but I've sort o' got used to calling it home.

THAT'S BETTER!

Our regular series highlighting old-fashioned cures used by Rumoledew residents over several generations continues with these headache remedies from "Whistler's Father":

A little nutmeg, grated into a mug of boiling water, inhaled rather than drunk, often brings welcome relief. Some prefer a thimbleful of whisky rubbed sharply in the hands and held to the nose. Camomile and lavender are also useful.

The Muckspreader, 1957

3
THE NAME GAME

High-flying academics and low-profile amateurs have long enjoyed bouts of guessing how Rumoledew got its colourful name.

A school of thought pointing to Old Norse derivations was largely discredited when a professor of linguistics at the University of East Anglia emphasised how "Ramel's-dune" was far more likely to have been a coastal settlement.

There have been serious claims for Anglo-Saxon and Old English influences – with dun as a down or hill – while obvious similarities with Runhall and Runham led to a rash of new theories in the 1920s.

A recent addition to the suggestion list came about by accident at a seminar for health workers organised by Lower Puckaterry Primary Care Trust.

A delegate with a decidedly posh voice made the village sound like "Raremildew", which alerted prominent botanists and historians alike to an unexplained outbreak of rising damp in numerous local hovels during the Roman occupation.

The jury is still out on that one while the woman who sparked such debate has volunteered for special elocution lessons at a finishing school in Happisburgh.

That leaves the fanciful field still led by the Rev Titus Duxbumme, Rector of Rumoledew from 1699 until his enforced retirement in 1756.

This long-serving cleric carried a notorious reputation for lack of generosity in heavenly spirit or worldly goods towards his parishioners. He was dubbed "the parsimonious parson" as he cadged all the way through his years as father of the flock.

Naturally, our tight parson was not averse to accepting "gifts" from smugglers venturing inland from their coastal fleshpots. He promised a "good word from on high" in return should retribution befall his regular providers.

On one famous occasion as he waited for nocturnal service among the gravestones at St Bartholomew's a voice whispered loudly: "Regrets, sire, but tubs of gin, brandy and whiskey have not come our way. Wilt thou accept this bottled bounty instead?"

"Yea, verily" replied the parson.... "Rum'll do!"

And it came to pass that a Customs and Exercise officer hiding in the bushes took that as the name of the village for his official report.

A few killjoys still maintain the whole business has nothing to do with Old English, Old Norse, Old Nick or Old Pals. They simply wave the flag for CMN – Comparatively Modern Norfolk.

A strange business or, as they say in more enlightened parts of the county, a rum ole dew. But I tend to side with the Customs and Exercise on this occasion.*

* They were called Customs and Exercise men in Norfolk in those days because they had to run a lot to catch up with the smugglers.

4
FIRST WITH NEWS

Enid Trett runs the combined village shop and post office, fully aware their days could be numbered. She took over in the early 1980s when her husband died of a heart attack at 32. Enid relishes her role at the hub of local life despite drastic changes and strong competition from new technology and town supermarkets.

I suppose the best thing about having a business like mine is being first with the village news. What customers don't tell me, they tell each other just loud enough for me to hear.

It's nearly 30 years since I took over from dear old Gladys Spring. I used to help her out at weekends and it seemed perfectly natural to go behind the counter full-time when she called it a day. She told me then how much she'd miss all the gossip: "Goes with the job. Cheers up the dullest of days. People are so funny but most of 'em don't even know it." Gal Gladys, your words ring so true and help keep me going whenever I feel like packing it all in.

Naturally, a lot of rumours start in my place and I have to be

THE PLOT THICKENS
ALONG THE ROWS

Digger, our regular gardening expert, is ready with another crop of useful tips. Remember, no correspondence can be entered into but the editor will be happy to receive any excess of flowers or vegetables resulting from advice given in this publication.

- Don't throw away your empty seed packets. They are often just the right size for storing your crop.
- Remember, the best time to take cuttings is when no-one is looking.
- A humane way to repel moles is to detach the battery operated cell from a musical greetings card and drop it into the excavation.
- To stop a neighbour's cat scratching up your garden, concrete one or the other over.
- Rummaging in an overgrown garden usually turns up a bouncy ball.
- If you want to tease your plants, water them with ice cubes.
- Don't forget, the family that rakes together, aches together.
- If you want to be an armchair gardener, just turn it over in your mind.
- If someone tells you your potatoes are on the small side this year, tell them you grow 'em to fit your mouth, not theirs.
- Don't get too excited before the annual flower show or you'll be accused of wisteria.

The Muckspreader, 1976

careful not to associate too freely with those behind the more scurrilous of them. "That's what they're saying in the shop" is a usual opener for a bit of scandal ready to be embellished a dozen times before sunset. Start one rumour – get one free! I usually nod and smile at the latest tittle-tattle rather than join in.

Young mums calling in after taking their children to school tend to be the biggest gossips, their imaginations fired no doubt by what they've seen and heard on television soaps the night before. Reckon it's one way of spicing up rather monotonous lives – some of them don't have a regular man about the house – but you can't help wondering what their offspring will be like when they grow up.

Most of my older customers come in for a mardle as much as anything. People forget how loneliness can seep into village life. Long-time neighbours die or move away and commuting strangers move in. Pensioners born in the parish are left on their own. They look forward to receiving another complicated form to be filled in so they can come and see me for a chat and a bit of company. The chair up the corner is always ready.

You see, the local shop can be an extension of social services – and that must stand as one of the main reasons to keep it open. I know you can get most items a bit cheaper in the supermarkets. I appreciate the information highway may soon make my little post office redundant. I accept that my outlook is based largely on homely tradition and affection for my native patch.

But what price can we put on community involvement, personal service and genuine caring for each other? That's what my business is all about and I suppose it's been that way ever since a village store first opened on the site in mid-Victorian times.

I dread the thought that I may be the last to help Rumoledew in this way, even those who only come in for a second-class stamp or tin of peas or just pay a call when snowdrifts mean they can't go anywhere else. They always look a bit embarrassed when I ask if I can help.

I fully intend to retire in the village where I was born. I don't drive, so it would be more than handy to have a shop on my doorstep. And I could keep up with all the gossip...

Now, something about me that should come as a surprise to my customers. I have a passion for poetry – it goes back to schooldays when we learnt new verses by heart every week and recited them in class – and I manage to scribble down a few lines of my own every day after work. Often I will use something I've heard or seen in the shop as my inspiration. Gladys was so right about people saying funny things without realising.

Perhaps I needed poetry as a sort of spiritual support when my husband died tragically young and I found real comfort in the verses of Christina Rossetti. I want these lines to be read at my funeral:

> *When I am dead, my dearest,*
> *Sing no sad songs for me;*
> *Plant thou no roses at my head,*
> *Nor shady cypress tree;*
> *Be the green grass above me,*
> *With showers and dewdrops wet;*
> *And if thou wilt, remember,*
> *And if thou wilt, forget.*

You can't spend so many years living and working in one place without wondering what might have been had fate dealt a different hand. Then, if you've got any sense, it's best to shrug your shoulders, clear your head, smile and give thanks for being part of proper Norfolk life.

Reckon my book of Rumoledew rhymes, hopefully to be published on my retirement, ought to be called Counter Attractions. Don't know how many more years I might have listening, watching and serving. But I aim to make the most of them.

HARVEST GIRLS

The recent display of old photographs, Rumoledew Remembers, attracted big crowds to the village hall.

We were delighted to play a leading part in this exciting parish project by contributing memory-stirrers from our files.

Scenes from farming past were especially popular, none more than this one provided by Walter Grimes. Land Army Girls helped to bring home the wartime harvest on Holly Farm — and Walter was glad of more attractive company than usual!

He told The Muckspreader: "I did have to moderate my language, but the mawthers liked a bit o'squit. Good workers as well. They earned their corn."

The Muckspreader, 2007

PUSSY POTION

Here's a pet cure passed on to us by animal-lover Mrs J. Gambling:

"If a cat requires medicine after eating something disagreeable, just dip one of its feet in castor oil. It's sure to lick it."

The Muckspreader, 1959

STILL WAITING

There are three raffle prizes still waiting to be claimed from the highly successful church garden fete.

They are: a bottle of homemade damson wine (yellow ticket 171); a voucher for a free home visit by a chiropodist (yellow ticket 256) and a copy of "New Light on the Psalms", kindly donated by the Rector, (pink 53).

Please take winning tickets to the Rectory to claim prize.

The Muckspreader, 1963

TOO NOISY?

Overheard at church social: "I shall have to give Holy Commotion a miss next Sunday."

The Muckspreader, 2001

GARDENING SLIP

The article on rose cultivation in our last edition may have caused come confusion when it was stated that you need "a loam containing plenty of humans." This should, of course, have read: "humus". We apologise.

The Muckspreader, 1982

5
SPECIAL AGENT

The Rev Kevin "Dick" Barton, an energetic young bachelor, looks after six churches with St Bartholomew's in Rumoledew the mother building in his group. Trained and ordained in his home city of Birmingham, this is his first taste of rural living.

I arrived in Norfolk a couple of years ago – and I'm still getting used to country people and their ways. So different from the pace and bustle of big-city life although there's no shortage of demands on my time serving six wonderful parish churches.

My first task was to find out why so many older members of my congregations called me "Dick" as I settled in. They seemed genuinely surprised that I hadn't heard of the special agent whose adventures on the radio held them spellbound after tea for several years. Well, I wasn't born when that Dick Barton took on the forces of evil – but I don't mind being cast as a modern equivalent wearing a dog collar.

As a newcomer, with a slight accent to betray my Birmingham roots, I soon realised it must be foolish and dan-

CONFESSIONAL BOX
Marcus Frost

This edition of Confessional Box, in which a well-known local character is encouraged to give straight answers to straight questions, features Marcus Frost. He has been a leading light of the Rumoledew Players as actor and producer for many years.

We raise the curtain on his colourful role in local life with an obvious inquiry:

Would you describe yourself as a show-off? – I would prefer to be acknowledged as a sensitive soul of artistic temperament who is perfectly at home in the public spotlight. I have always been blessed with a surfeit of self- confidence.

Marcus Frost, pictured during his early days in repertory

Can you recall your first performance on stage? – Yes, as a seven-year-old playing Peter Pan in a school production described by the local newspaper's drama critic as "a dazzling diversion to Never-Never Land on the wings of vivid imagination."

And your favourite role so far? – Hard to choose between Charley's Aunt and Dame Dome. I played the former in repertory at Scarborough in 1962 and the latter in our village pantomime millennium production Round the Horning with Dick Barton Turf. It's wonderful to suspend all sense of reality and play a member of the opposite sex. I have been commended for my taste in dresses.

What is your proudest achievement? – Convincing Rumoledew Players that rehearsals are necessary before retiring to the pub.

Your biggest regret? – Failing to convince some would-be performers that rehearsals function better when lines have been learnt.

What, if anything, would you change about the village? – I would outlaw idle gossip about last night's television. As a non-driver, I call for more regular bus services and a fish-and-chip van to visit at least twice a week.

How would you like to be remembered? As a genial soul who took his cue to enliven the village stage.

Take a bow, Marcus!   *The Muckspreader, 2001* gerous to preach radical change in an area where certain things have been done in certain ways over a considerable period of time. One long-serving churchwarden took me to one side at an early parochial church council meeting and hinted gently in his broad Norfolk brogue: "We'll tell yew when yew git it wrong".

He and other equally subtle colleagues have helped keep me on the straight and narrow, avoiding "trendy ideas" designed to alienate the hard core who like their worship conducted in a traditional and comfortable manner. I fully respect this feeling – but we must do something to attract younger folk into our churches. God does not restrict His bounty to pensioners.

The use of pop songs at funerals, weddings and christenings has been the subject of considerable debate. I have gone along with some requests – I Did It My Way can be a highly suitable testimony at the farewell service for a strong-minded local character – but there's a growing tendency to take the reverence out of important occasions. I simply could not sanction Another One Bites the Dust at a wedding last summer.

We are working hard to organise more social events in our churches, especially in the parishes where there's no other community meeting place. I was particularly pleased with support for a home-grown Question Time in St Peter's at Lower Puckaterry – although some of the language aimed at the men who wanted to double the size of the hamlet by encouraging developers from Essex left something to be desired.

My lay readers are dedicated and versatile; we have two accomplished organists, Ethel Granger and Boris Marchant, who play at as many services as possible. Both are in their seventies and sadly there are no apparent successors waiting in the wings. A familiar story in rural areas, along with the constant challenge to come up with new ideas for fundraising.

St Bartholomew's tower is in need of urgent repairs with over £70,000 required just to get work started. Bring-and-buy stalls and jumble sales do their bit, but it takes something like the Rumoledew Rave to get the whole village involved.

It was young George Billings' idea to challenge every family to put their talents on display at a major weekend event held in a marquee next to the church. They had to attract sponsors and accept the judges' decision as final with the winners being invited to represent the village in a gala county extravaganza on the Norfolk Showground.

Over £5,000 was raised as the Billings family came out on top with their dynamic mixture of charades on roller skates, spinning plates on walking sticks and presenting their River Dance in sou'westers and rubber boots.

Such enterprise gives me great hope that we can continue to utilise all churches in the group. We could do with proper heating in three of them – it is difficult to enthuse about Moses and the burning bush when you're suffering from frostbite – but each has its own distinctive character and charm.

So, now its time to pop into the confessional and tell my congregations something about me that isn't commonly known. I'm sure they wouldn't guess from the way I take it so gently round the twisting country lanes in my Ford Focus.

I have a passion for speed. Or, to be more precise, I used to zoom about the place on a high-powered motor cycle in my Birmingham days. The local newspaper dubbed me "The Quicker Vicar", "the Faster Pastor" and "the Revving Rev."

God sent me to Norfolk to slow down. I sold my machine, but kept my leathers, helmet and goggles. Just in case I need a few props when I preach a sermon about David's Triumph being heard throughout Israel.

6
A BRIGHT FUTURE

Frances Potter is headteacher at the village primary school, flourishing again after falling numbers and several threats of closure. She hails from Norwich – while her colleague, Greg Palmer, is a Suffolk lad from Ipswich. This gives rise to plenty of friendly rivalry in and out of the classroom.

It was always my ambition to take charge of a primary school in the country and the Rumoledew Academy – as my city friends call it – fills the bill perfectly. Several families with young children have moved into the village in recent years to give the register a healthy glow.

I began my teaching days in Norwich, so I have been lucky enough to spend all my career so far in my home county. At least I don't need an interpreter when one of the pupils breaks into a broad Norfolk accent. The other week we were treated to "Cor, blarst me, that ent harf a soler!" by a home-grown lad extolling the virtues of a fat hedgehog discovered in the playground. A "soler" is anything surprisingly large in size.

SCHOOL WRITING
COMPETITION

We are extremely grateful to Frances Potter, headteacher at our flourishing village school, for organising a writing competition on behalf of this publication.

Her pupils were asked to compose a short essay entitled "What I Like About Rumoledew". We will feature the best, starting with this highly commended effort from nine-year-old Sophie Craske:

I have lived here all my life and I know now why my Dad says it is better than anywhere else. We all know each other but still get on quite well.

My Dad reckons the pub is really cool and I did see the windows open when I went past. My Mum says the shop is handy for things you forget to buy at the supermarket.

Our school is nice. My horrible brother is in another class but he pulls faces at playtime. He has a packed lunch. So I have hot.

I would like to marry someone kind and have lots of children to keep our school open. I don't mind if my brother goes to live somewhere else.

Our class made up a rhyme to go with our dancing at the fete. We sang "Rumoledew, we love you!" But not too loud in case we got told off.

The Muckspreader, 2009

CALLS REJECTED

Calls for Rumoledew to enter the Best Kept Village Competition next year were rejected by the parish council. "We are not a chocolate-box community – although we may have a very soft centre" said councillor Harold Boldero. The vote was 8 – 1 against.

The Muckspreader, 1969

This presented me with a perfect opportunity to introduce other dialect words into our nature study lessons. "Bishy-barney-bee" for ladybird and "dodman" for snail are regular favourites, but "pollywiggle" for tadpole, "harnser" for heron and "stannickle" for stickleback are colourful additions to our list on the wall.

Despite the restraints of the National Curriculum, and constant changes we are asked to make, I feel room should be found for local characteristics and parochial pride.

Most of my school governors agree... although one lady insists we put every emphasis on the Queen's English. I may have caused some confusion by suggesting that Walter Grimes and our beloved monarch have much in common as they both say "orff" for "off", "lorst" for "lost" and "horsepittle" for "hospital". Now there's linguistic equality for you!

Several of the village's older residents, who attended this school as far back as the 1920s, drop in on occasions to tell the children what life was like locally before television, electricity, hot and cold running water and other things we now take for granted. Arthur Laycock raised a lot of laughs with stories about the honeycart collecting pails from little buildings down the yard.

This sort of get-together helps to close the generation gaps which can give cause for concern even in a pleasant community like Rumoledew. One of my favourite teachers in Norwich, Miss Corbett, often remarked that those who had a good idea where they came from stood the best chance of knowing where they might be going.

We try hard to instil a sense of belonging into our pupils, to make them aware of village heritage based largely on a living from the land. Some youngsters do have to be told that eggs, meat and milk don't come originally from the supermarket. That's where Walter Grimes comes in handy with his wonderful farming stories, rolling back the years but always making comparisons with today.

He and Tickler Haynes cut the ribbon to open our brand new indoor toilets a couple of years ago. The old part of the school was built in 1896. As Walter said at the ceremony "Thass a bloomin' long while ter hev yar legs crorsst!"

Much is made in the village of the fact that I come from Norwich, while my colleague Greg Palmer is an Ipswich product. It's inevitable, therefore, that we must show our true sporting colours and loyalties when a football local derby comes along. I've alerted the children to the real danger of being too partisan in their support, but it's mostly good, clean fun when the yellow and green Canaries taken on the Tractor Boys in blue.

Greg is a season-ticket holder at Portman Road and loves to stir it up if his team are doing better than City. I'm much more circumspect in showing allegiance... and there is a very good reason for that.

It's time to reveal my little secret from the headteacher's dugout. It's not Norwich City or Ipswich Town results I look out for first on a Saturday teatime. I'm more interested in how Burnley have got on.

It goes back to my time at teacher training college when I went out with Mark, a fellow student passionate about the Clarets. He took me to see them in action at Turf Moor as icy rain needled in from the Pennines. Burnley won 4 – 0 – and I didn't feel the cold. Although our relationship didn't go into extra time after we left college, I still have a soft spot for him and his beloved club. Well, I do tell the children that loyalty is important.

The future for our primary school looks bright after several years of deep worry. There was talk of closure and becoming part of a federation with certain buildings staying open elsewhere to cater for neighbouring villages. Thankfully, the Rumoledew Academy strides on into its second century, a vital part of a community where "a good grounding "has long been much more than a useful idea.

Our Ofsted report last year prompted a warm glow of satisfaction – "This is a happy school with bright, inquisitive children clearly relishing their rural connections."

I just hope a fair number of them can eventually find homes and jobs to allow them to stay close to those roots.

CAN YOU HELP?

Here's a cheerful gathering of Rumoledew residents – but can anyone tell us what they're up to?

It's thought the picture was taken in the early 1920s and it looks as if the revellers are preparing for some sort of fete or carnival. Those at the front are clearly dressed up with somewhere to go.

Please get in touch if you have any information that can help us date and identify the event.

The Muckspreader, 1996

CRICKET FACTS
AND FIGURES

We are indebted to Ernie Grint, scorer and statistician for Rumoledew Cricket Club, for unveiling these vital gems of information from his extensive records:

The modern club was formed in 1920, with Sir John Neville-Pratt as chairman, captain and benefactor, although it is believed the game was played regularly in the village before the first world war. No official records survive.

Rumoledew won the Dodman Cup 20-overs knock-out competition in 1929, beating Puckaterry Parva by 12 runs in the final. This was the club's first trophy success.

Two players share the honour of taking hat-tricks in cup contests, both during the 1959 season. Hedley Gladwell achieved the feat against Old Millpondians in the first round of the Pollywiggle Trophy and Tweaker Holmes followed suit in round two against Cloverloke Poultry.

Bisto Bailey holds the record for most centuries in a season. He hit six in the 1948 campaign. His 147 not out against Barleysele included 19 sixes, another club best. A farm accident the following year cut short a promising career.

Hedley Gladwell, who retired in 1976, missed only one match in the 28 successive seasons he played for the club. He was ruled out of an away fixture against Bottlebump in 1967 when his only daughter Amanda insisted on being married on a Saturday afternoon in June.

Two village parsons have turned out for the club. The Rev Egbert Trotter played three games in 1934, scoring a total of 17 runs, while the Rev Paul Hipperson managed four overs of leg-spin at the start of the 1951 season before a dislocated shoulder ended his playing days. His bowling figures probably add up to a Rumoledew record, 4 – 0 – 68 – 0.

Albert Myreson holds the record for most catches in a season – 41 in 1963, 38 of them as wicket keeper. His brother, Gerald, also a wicket keeper, made a record 19 stumpings in 1969.

Biggest total in the club's history came against a touring side from Nottinghamshire in 1983. Rumoledew piled up 386 – 4 declared. Their opponents, treated to a lavish barbecue and beer-

The Rev. Egbert Trotter, who played three times for Rumoledew CC in the 1934 season

tasting at The Four Ferrets on the eve of the match, replied with 35.

Umpires, of course, are neutral. But one official attached to the club in the 1950s was asked to stand down after a series of controversial incidents. Cedric Gunn, invariably known as "Trigger", upheld 13 lbw appeals in one match, nine of them in favour of the home team. Although he whittled it down to 12 and 11 in the next two fixtures, he was persuaded to hand over the white coat to Barney Minster. Poor eyesight encouraged him to raise the finger only if all three stumps went flying.

The Muckspreader, 2002

CONFESSIONAL BOX
Ethel Granger

The Rumoledew group of six churches are served admirably by organists Ethel Granger and Boris Marchant. Ethel, who began playing at St Bartholomew's 45 years ago, has agreed to enter our Confessional Box to give straight answers to straight questions.

Do you come from a musical family? Not really. My sister Grace and I had piano lessons while we were at the village school, but she gave up to play tennis while I carried on.

Which is your favourite organ in the group? It has to be St Bartholomew's. That's where I started and where I feel most at home. Lovely acoustics in the church so the organ doesn't fight the congregation.

Your favourite hymn? The Lord's My Shepherd, to the tune of Crimond. Perfect for all occasions. My mother had it for her wedding and funeral. Everyone knows it.

Do you have any glaring faults? Well, some would see it as a fault, but I prefer to consider it a reasonable trait. I can be very abrupt with people who only come to church on special occasions and then try to tell you how to run the place. I also eat too much ginger cake.

What would you change in the village? The price of ginger cake in the shop. I say make it too expensive for humble organists! And make it illegal for car radios to be heard on the street. Just one more hideous noise we have to suffer these days.

What happens when you and Boris Marchant retire? I don't know. There are no obvious successors waiting to take over. So we'll have to keep going for as long as possible.

How would you like to be remembered? As a willing servant of the community who played most of the right notes in the right order.

Thanks for the music, Ethel!

The Muckspreader, 2009

7
KEEPING PEACE

Clifford Gaskin, chairman of the parish council, is a member of one of Rumoledew's oldest-established farming families. A steady and reliable character, he brings experience and tact to the major role of keeping the peace between native and newcomer.

An old Norfolk saying runs: "If you want to stay friends with people in your village, keep off the parish council". Well, like my father before me, I've had plenty of chances to test the truth of that!

There are times when I reckon I must be barmy to leave the fresh air and peace of a 20-acre field or the gentle rhythm of the milking parlour for a parish meeting, full of short tempers and long speeches going nowhere. I implore them all to go "through the chair", but too many insist on talking through the backs of their necks.

I have to stay calm and polite, of course, even if local democracy is on the verge of anarchy. It's remarkable how many confrontations cane be diffused with a few quietly-spoken words.

My favourite trick in the hot seat is to repeat deliberately but gently some of the more outlandish comments just made by council colleagues or others in the hall... when they hear their own excesses coming back at them like that, they usually feel embarrassed enough to apologise and cool off.

A lot of the frustration to surface at our meetings stems from limited powers invested in parish councils. We try to make decisions and recommendations in the interests of our own community and the immediate neighbourhood, but district councils, the county council and the big bad wolves at Westminster can stick all kinds of spanners in the village works. Perfectly good ideas and sensible plans are all too often swept aside by those who think they know what's best for us in the sticks.

Take affordable housing, surely the only real hope for young people who want to stay in the area where their parents and grandparents lived and worked. They're bound to feel angry and neglected when permission is granted instead for "executive dwellings" aimed at rich incomers.

Still, we have managed to attract a number of young families in recent years, a few of them to The Pastures, our new estate with the country feel, Not many villages of our size can boast a full set of school, village hall, shop and post office, church and pub. We must be doing something right despite regular murmurs about "that lot on the council who talk too much and do too little."

It is quite a job to keep the peace between occasionally belligerent newcomers and constantly cussed natives. We have a fair mixture on the parish council – and it does appear that some of them seek election in order to enjoy a good argument without spending money in the pub.

Calls to "move with the times" from recent arrivals are answered with "yes, but we don't want to hoss along at 100 miles an hour!" by Rumoledew stalwarts. I try to steer both factions along the road to compromise in order to avoid fiery stalemate over contentious matters like planning.

Some long-time residents view every new development as another nail in the community coffin, but I remind them that this means someone fresh to disagree with. The shrewder newcomers are learning how to come up with bright ideas ... and then convince hardened locals they thought of them first. Adaptable thinking at grass-roots level.

Perhaps my biggest worry is Rumoledew might turn eventually into a bland settlement for highly-qualified commuters or well-heeled retired who like the idea of being relatively close to nature. More farms are likely to disappear with land being sold off for building – my sons have no interest in taking over when I call it a day – and that must further change the face of our countryside.

In the meantime it is up to parish councils, whatever their flavour, to do what they can to keep small communities on the right track, absorbing inevitable changes into a proven framework.

I truly believe I have made more friends than enemies since becoming chairman in the early 1990s. I know my diplomatic traits have improved considerably, although the awkward member who insists on all minutes of the previous meeting being read before every fresh adventure does try my patience.

Now for a little something about me that isn't generally known. Regular callers at Drift Farm may have noticed a distinct absence of geese. Well, that's because I am dreadfully scared of the creatures.

LETTER TO EDITOR

It is not customary to publish a letter without giving a full name and address. I have been furnished with full details by this correspondent and, in this case, will afford anonymity to forestall any possibility of reprisals or victimisation. Important issues are raised and this could well prove to be a catalyst for other views in this publication and a meaningful debate within our community.

I feel compelled to register my utter disgust at certain comments given prominence in reports of a recent meeting of our parish council.

Newcomers to this area in general and to this village in particular were described by one councillor as "blow-ins". While this may have been delivered with a modicum of humour, I found it insulting, sounding as if people like myself were some kind of sub-species bent on destroying this green and pleasant land.

The same councillor also dropped in the unpleasant label of "furriner" while referring to the need for more affordable housing. At best, this smacks of rampant protectionism, at worst, very close to racism.

We live in a free country where people can move where and when they like. Norfolk cannot have special rules and restrictions of its own. This parish needs fresh blood to keep its heart pumping into the next century.

I moved here hoping to play a part in that process, not to fend off unwarranted attacks on my integrity and background.

The Muckspreader, 1999

Bulls, billy-goats and rams can do their worst and I won't give a tinker's cuss. But the very sight of a goose on the loose brings me out in a cold sweat. It goes back to childhood when a bad-tempered gander attached itself to my left arm for no reason other than I had prodded it with a stick.

My shrieks of terror brought father racing from the bullock shed to separate my limb from the flapping devil with a hungry beak. I asked if we could have goose for a change at Christmas that year.

So, perhaps the only way to unnerve me as chairman of the parish council is to send in a disgruntled colleague with a long neck and rasping hiss to make the feathers fly.

RECTOR'S CALL

The Rector informs us that as maintenance of the church-yard is becoming increasingly difficult and expensive, it would be much appreciated if parishioners can cut the grass around their own graves.

The Muckspreader, 1961

APOLOGIES

We must apologise sincerely for three topographical errors in our "From the Rector's Chair" article in our last edition.

The serpent in the Garden of Eden "crept" upon the scene and not as printed.

God destroyed the cities of Sodom and Gomorrah, not "Sod'em and Gomorrah".

And the commandment should have read: "Thou shalt not commit adultery", instead of "Thou shalt not admit adultery."

The Muckspreader, 1958

PARISH COUNCIL TRENDYSPEAK

A local resident, actually fed up because, basically, someone kept moving the goalposts, decided to open fresh windows of opportunity in rural areas at this moment in time.

He visited a dozen villages in the Rumoledew area to search for favourite clichés, preferably fairly new, heard at parish council meetings in the past year.

Poorly parrots, trips over the moon and icing on cakes were disqualified, but his top 10 proves this district can be as trendy as the next. One-word alternatives are offered as part of a steep learning curve:

On the back burner – forgotten

Quality time – holiday

Lost the plot – drunk

Really up for it – pushy

Get their act together – cheat

Flavour of the month – creep

Chosen vocation – lumbered

Set the agenda – pontificate

Dead in the water – drowned

End of the day – bedtime

The Muckspreader, 2006

8
DRAMA QUEEN

Belinda Arthurton, a glamorous divorcee, is a former actress at the heart of Rumoledew's cultural and social life. She's a leading light in the local drams society and writes and produces the annual village pantomime.

I know what they call me – "The Blonde Bombshell" – and I suppose I ought to be flattered. At least it's better than most of the titles pinned on me during my Berkshire days. Jealous wives shouldn't have talented husbands who want to shed inhibitions on the stage.

Life is much more relaxed in Norfolk. I came because it's on the road to nowhere, although that should not preclude a dramatic diversion or two along the way.

Yes, Rumoledew Players are more Aykbourn than Anouilh, more madness than method, at present, but I nurse fond hopes we could yet bless Beckett, Ibsen, Ionesco and Pirandello with a rich Norfolk accent!

"They like a nice comedy" said Marcus Frost, leading man or producer for most performances when I arrived eight years ago. "Well, perhaps they should try a good comedy" I retorted after watching a couple of pot-boilers and a version of Dry Rot that lent itself too easily to comments about dead wood.

A Midsummer Night's Dream, the first Shakespeare offering in the society's long history, didn't blow all the cobwebs away but it opened up a new front in the group's ambitions.

It used to be customary for these who turned up and volunteered for readings to take all the parts. It was very cosy and predictable. I introduced proper auditions, including chances for would-be thespians from neighbouring parishes.

Dark accusations of cultivating a clique of newcomers to take the juiciest roles still persist on occasions, although extra variety and much bigger audiences suggest the "new" approach is working.

Perhaps our biggest success to date was a week-long run of Roots, Arnold Wesker's play set in Norfolk. While some of the author's more subtle nuances may not have come through, he would have been thrilled by a chorus of truly authentic voices. Mike Boldero's portrayal of rustic Stan Mann brought the house down every night,

I had no hesitation in casting "proper" local players soaked in Norfolk ways for this one. That brought mutterings about favouring the "old guard" – you simply can't win! – but it soon became obvious how this play could only come alive with home-grown fervour. Squit and polish, I call it.

Squit, that peculiarly Norfolk brand of humour, sometimes dry to the point of being arid, often totally lost on newcomers not used to slowing down, listening and thinking, takes pride of place in the annual village pantomime. It must go well above a few heads – but no-one's prepared to own up for fear of being dismissed as "thrippence short of a shillin'".

I picked that one up from Mike Boldero, a rich source of old

sayings coated in Norfolk dialect. He's my main script consult-
ant from the beginning of December as work starts on the
village "blood-letting" exercise culminating in three sell-out
performances at the turn of the year.

I also work closely with Alec Paine, editor of The
Muckspreader magazine, to make sure all local topics – and reasonable slices of scandal – get an airing.

Laughing at themselves is a healthy Rumoledew tradition,
with the vicar and chairman of the parish council making guest
panto appearances to prove they're no better than the rest

Last year's offering, Little Red Riding Hood and the
Thickening Plot, made much of a drawn-out village argument
over who was entitled to allotments. My next target is likely to
be dog-fouling on the playing field. Stand by for David
Beckham Goes Through the Motions.

I like to think I've mucked in with Norfolk village life, even
though a few true locals still reckon I'm a bit different, a bit
posh, because I used to be a professional actress. Maybe I'll be
fully accepted when I've perfected that lovely local accent. It's
very hard to do... just listen to some of the laughable attempts
on television and radio.

So now it's curtain up on a little secret I brought with me to
the fleshpots of Rumoledew. Early in my career, when money
and opportunities were very limited, I agreed to take part in
what I believe is now called an "adult movie".

Frankly, it was rather tame fare with everyone else in the cast
as bored as me. This epic was entitled Lust Horizon and I
played an erotic dancer (or was it an exotic prancer?) called
Norma Stitz.

I never saw the finished product. Thankfully, I've never met
anyone who has.

BARROW FULL OF LAUGHS

We are pleased to publish another outstanding Norfolk yarn from Mike Boldero's extensive collection, some of which find their way into the annual village pantomime.

Granfar's old mate, Horry thought he'd go in for pig keeping, and he bought himself an old sow and put her out in the back yard.

Couple of weeks later, they met in the pub. Granfar say: "How's that old sow gettin' on?" Horry say: "Well, all she keep a'dewin' is rollin' about in the mud." Granfar say: "That mean she's riddy fer the boar. Charlie down the loke, he's got an old boar. He charge £5 a time for his sarvices. You'd better take har down there ter git sarviced."

Next morning Horry put the sow in his wheelbarrow and pushed her down to Charlie's. He handed over his £5 and the old boar did his business.

Horry says to Charlie: "How do I know if thass took?" Charlie replied: "Dew yew look out the window in the mornin'. If she's standin' up, eatin' grass, she'll be in pig, but if she's still rollin' abowt in the mud, thass no good, yew'll hatter bring har back."

Horry looked out of the window next morning and there was the sow still rolling around in the mud. So he put her back in the wheelbarrow, returned to Charlie's for another £5-worth. Next morning Horry said to his missus: "I carn't bear ter look. Jist yew garp out the window. Is that old sow still rollin' abowt in the mud?"

"No," she say. "Thass good. Is she standin' up eatin' grass?"

"No," she say. "Well, woss she a'dewin', then?" say Horry.

"Oh," say his missus, "She's a'sittin' in the wheelbarrer!"

The Muckspreader, 1986

9
MINE HOST

Gerry Wilson is landlord of The Four Ferrets pub, while his wife, Jean looks after the restaurant side of the business. They have two children, Trevor (8) and Marie (6), both pupils at the village school. Gerry and Jean met while working for an insurance company in Norwich.

When people ask why I keep a pub, I tell them it's more a case of working hard enough for it to keep me and my family. Make no mistake; these are tough times in the trade, even for a popular watering-hole in a pleasant village.

We took over before the recession, smoking ban and other little considerations designed to call "time" on so many pubs across the country. To be fair, I've noticed in old Norfolk directories that many of my predecessors at The Four Ferrets had to taken on other jobs to make ends meet. For example, Henry Gage, landlord in the early 1900s, was also the village blacksmith and pig slaughterer.

Perhaps our restaurant, The Munching Mawkin, is the modern extra, although, like most country pubs nowadays we have to serve food to stay afloat. To be brutally honest, the "salt-of-the-earth" customers who want nothing more than a half of bitter and a mardle don't keep us in business. We survive largely on regular diners and drinkers, several of them comfortably-off newcomers from The Pastures, the estate where Norfolk accents are about as rare as complaints about my wife's cooking.

Her shepherd's pie – "made with fresh shepherds" – and gooseberry crumble – "only for the sturdy constitution" – are biggest favourites on the menu. Local pensioners enjoy a special lunch for a fiver on Wednesdays with a free sweet for those who do a party piece. It keeps them off the streets!

I suppose any pub worth its salted peanuts should double as the local parliament. The parish council provides the rubber stamp and official jargon but The Four Ferrets is the real policy-making arena. It's hard keeping order at times – several regulars bring their own wooden spoons and use them most effectively – but a lively debate can double my takings in an evening.

Best contests are between the Bolt-hole Brigade, who want to change everything, and the Gnarled Natives, who want to keep everything in place... except the Bolt-hole Brigade. There is an element of grudging respect growing between these two factions as well as a tendency to wind each other up just for the sheer hell of it.

I try to adopt a neutral stance as befits a lad lucky enough to be born and raised in Plymouth before moving to work in Norfolk and then stamping my passport by wooing and marrying a local girl. Jean, of course, is heavily biased in favour of the old guard. Our children are slightly confused but they'll have to learn to find the right balance in a fast-changing world.

Monday quiz nights at the pub were supposed to help build

bridges between old and new as well as introducing more voluble contestants to the subtle art of thinking in silence. It has only worked up to a point. When Mike Boldero sets the questions, there are a lot to do with Norfolk dialect and old customs. Nathan Sowerby tends to specialise in exciting facts about his home county of Lancashire.

Nathan calls it "useful cross-fertilisation after centuries of inbreeding". I reckon this process will reach a peak when Taffy Morgan and Paddy Doyle do the honours.

We do have a pool table in the back room and I did try a couple of live music nights last year, but this isn't really a young people's pub. There's a flourishing youth club at the village hall where loud music doesn't upset so many people as it would if unleashed regularly in my main bar.

It's often a matter of sensible compromise in small places like this and I can't afford to upset people who live nearby. Open warfare inside the pub can be confined and managed. I prefer to call it valuable missionary work.

How do I see the future for pubs like mine? Well, overheads are bound to keep on rising along with the price of beers and spirits. Only the brave will survive, diversifying (just like the farmers) to meet fresh demands.

More people who like country life will be able to work from home, so young professionals can put the emphasis on community rather than commuting. That must mean the pub becoming even more of a social hub with an even wider cosmopolitan base. Sorry, Gnarled Natives, but the wind of change causing your smocks to billow could well turn into a hurricane in the next few years.

Village pub landlords are honour-bound to keep secrets prone to slip out when drink is in. I'll wait until it's time to write my memoirs before spilling the spicy beans. But my own little secret can be revealed now without hurting anyone... an aversion to the taste and smell of any spirits.

It goes back to the night I met Jean at a party in Norwich soon after my arrival to take on a new job in insurance. I tried to impress her by knocking back everything on offer, including half a bottle of whiskey. I passed out while she was explaining how she got into the insurance business.

She helped me recover from that embarrassing predicament. We are well on the way to living happily ever after in the Norfolk sunshine.

THE RECTOR REFLECTS

We must all realise the value of tact in awkward circumstances.

I'm reminded of the rector's wife who looked out of the window to see a familiar figure coming up the garden path.

She called to her husband: "William, here comes that awful bore, Mrs Merryweather. I suppose she's come to discuss the more recent sins of our blessed parishioners. You had better disappear to your study upstairs."

The rector did so. After nearly an hour of listening and nodding, his wife excused herself and went to take the cat out to the kitchen to give it some milk.

William, noting the end of conversation and hearing the door open and close, assumed the coast was clear. He called over the banister: "I'll be down in a few moments, dear, now that awful woman has gone."

Unflustered, his wife replied in smart dulcet tones: "Oh, but you must come down at once, William. The awful woman went over an hour ago. Mrs Merryweather is here now."

The Muckspreader, 1973

10
COMING HOME

Martha Callaby is a retired nurse, a spinster "but not one of the miserable kind." She returned to the village to look after her aging mother in the 1980s and then decided to take over the family seat at Thistledown Cottage.

I feel very lucky to be living in the house where I was born and where my dear parents spent so many happy years.

Perhaps it's a bit large for one person, but I love the space inside and out. My garden and my chickens keep me busy and I never tire of those views of open countryside towards Drift Farm. I watch the seasons come and go.

My years working away from Rumoledew made me appreciate it all the more when I came home to nurse mother. She'd been there on her own for over 10 years after father died, so the old cottage was already used to individual tastes. Friends tell me it's just like me now – prim and proper!

The family graves in St Bartholomew's churchyard remind me how deep our roots go into this village soil. I celebrate rich lives with fresh flowers rather than stand mourning in the shadows. As Edith Trett often reminds customers in her shop, being over the hill is much better than being under it.

There are several people around here I grew up with, so my homecoming didn't just emphasise how much things have changed. The "old guard" will always complain about new-comers taking over, but you can find plenty of common ground if you look hard enough.

Most of those who move into a village like ours want the same things as us... a gentler pace of life, country walks, famil-iar faces, cheery greetings, caring more for each other. The awkward few, usually the noisiest, have to be converted grad-ually to more sensible ways.

I had to look after many difficult patients during my nursing career, some of them constantly complaining day and night. You learn how to deal with them. One man kept on whinging: "But it hurts when I do this." I went across, tucked him in and told him quietly not to do it, then.

The same sort of philosophy comes into play when new-comers to Rumoledew moan about cockerels crowing and manure smelling. I apologise on behalf of all rural residents – and advise them to find an estate agent specialising in high-rise flats.

Although I've been made very welcome by the congregation at St Bartholomew's, I still miss the old Methodist chapel where my parents worshipped regularly and I attended Sunday school. Unlike some of my young friends, I enjoyed learning recitations for the anniversary when we had a special preacher and a full house. The collection helped pay for our annual bus outing to Hunstanton.

Our superintendent, dear old Joseph Dixon, used to hand

out little brown envelopes from his waistcoat pocket on the way there, precious coins for donkey rides, ice creams and little presents to bring home. Happy times!

Youngsters today expect so much. I was an only child but never had more than I needed. Even now it seems wrong to buy anything for myself or anyone else just for the sake of it. "Waste not, want not" as my mother used to say.

As secretary for the Women's Institute (monthly meetings at the village hall) and publicity officer for the Church fundraising appeal, I get plenty of opportunities to exercise my joined-up writing. I do have a computer and printer for official letters and reports but I still enjoy using pen and ink. It's becoming a forgotten art – and I may have to give evening classes to keep it alive!

I am well organised, obviously a legacy of my nursing days, and determined to finish jobs once I've started. There's more than enough to do in this village. My cottage is the perfect refuge when I need to escape and spend time on my own.

Reading is one of the great joys of my life – and that's where my "secret side" comes in. I adore crime novels, especially those written by Agatha Christie, Dorothy L Sayers, Gladys Mitchell, Patricia Highsmith, P.D. James, Kate Ellis and Frances Fyfield. All women of intuition and style. How I envy their talents!

Perhaps the best tribute I can pay is to confess that they seriously tempt me into wanting to be the Miss Marple of Rumoledew, although we can do without too much violence.

I imagine being called to a meeting of the parochial church council to unmask the perpetrator of some heinous crime in the crypt or a gathering of the Women's Institute to reveal who has been poisoning the sausage rolls and iced buns.

Innocent chit-chat in the village shop suddenly takes on a

menacing edge. Familiar smiles cloak wicked intent. A flashing light near the churchyard is the signal for satanic rites. An owl's cry escaping from poplar trees on the edge of Drift Farm is a guilty call from the past...

Don't worry. Whenever these sort of escapades are on the march, it's time to make a strong cup of cocoa, draw the curtains and retire to bed with a good book.

MILKING TIME

Here's a memory-stirring scene from Rumoledew past – cows on their way along Tanner Lane to be milked at Primrose Farm. The row of thatched houses has long gone and it's thought the photograph dates back to the early 1920s.

The Muckspreader, 1984

11

LOCAL FLAVOUR

Russell Procter captains the village cricket club and The Zealots, one of the quartets contesting Monday quiz sessions at The Four Ferrets. He works in a solicitor's office in Norwich after moving to the county from Bedford five years ago.

We may not be the most successful team on the field in this part of Norfolk - but at least our teas finish top of the league every summer!

It's a subtle ploy to slow down unsuspecting visitors with outstanding refreshments. Rumoledew feasts, built round Emily Maitland's legendary flans, have been voted biggest and tastiest by all our opponents since I took over at the helm. Trouble is our batting order is too often gobbled up by wicket-hungry bowlers.

Curly Gladwell says we are going through a transitional period which started with his father's retirement to spend more time on the allotment in 1976. Tweaker Holmes reckons the club's youth policy faltered when National Service claimed too

BEACH BOYS
ON PARADE

A recent article on seaside outings prompted Clifford Gaskin of Drift Farm to dig out this fine photograph of him and brother Peter, on the left, enjoying a donkey ride at Hunstanton in 1938.

"We went to Sunny Hunny several times before the war and thoroughly lapped up long hours on the beach. Peter was a much more accomplished rider than me, so they always tended to put him on the more frisky creatures.

"He came to grief one summer when he was showing off a bit with his impression of Tom Mix rounding up the outlaws. His lively mount pulled up abruptly at the water's edge – and pitched Peter into the foam" said Clifford with a wry grin.

The Muckspreader, 1981

many victims. Scorer Ernie Grint puts it down to life's rich sporting cycle – "an' we hev got a rare slow puncture."

We had to join the league to keep a fixture list going but resisted the example of other clubs on our patch to import more talented players. Two of them in divisions above us employ overseas players from New Zealand and South Africa as full-time coaches sponsored by local businesses.

Rumoledew operates a strict policy of restricting membership to a six-mile radius in a bid to keep the "local" flavour alive. We are much admired for our old-fashioned stance at the crease, not least by those who get the chance of easy points towards promotion!

With cup competitions proliferating, there's not much room left for friendlies against clubs of similar stock. We did organise a brief tour of Lincolnshire last year but bad weather forced us to spend far too much time in cheerful social clubs and pubs.

I keep my competitive edge in shape with weekly quiz sessions at The Four Ferrets. My colleagues, Dick Cowper, John Sweet and Hughie Barnes, all work in Norwich offices and we share a car most weekdays for commuting to and fro. We swot up on our travels, but nothing can prepare for Mike Boldero's weird and wonderful Norfolk questions.

He takes great delight in befuddling all "furriners" round the bar with references to Boy John Letters and the Singing Postman hit parade in broad dialect tones.

We lost a recent contest to The Swedebashers because we didn't know "all of a muckwash" means hot and bothered and "on the slantendicular" suggests something isn't quite straight. Like the rules on Monday nights in our beloved local.

While some claim there are too many newcomers in the village, I thin the mix is quite healthy. Old stagers love to tell you how it's always been done and why. The "blow-ins", as Curly Gladwell calls anyone not born in Rumoledew, can open up windows blacked out since the war.

As cricket club representative on the village hall committee, I campaigned for proper cricket nets to be installed on the playing field to encourage more youngsters to take up the game. Their popularity means real hope for the future of our club as well as quieter streets and less vandalism around the place.

I remember how sport played a big part in my formative years in Bedford and helped curb so much anti-social behaviour in our area. "Take it out on spinners, not society" said dear old Horace Pickford.

I have been described as the village's most eligible bachelor, though that could have something to do with the fact my father is supposed to be a millionaire. He isn't, but his wholesale grocery business in Bedford provides a tidy living.

My training for the law led to Norwich, still a fine city compared to many, and I enjoy the best of both worlds by living in the country and involving myself in the community. Cricket offers the great escape from office routine – and I don't have to cook much at weekends if we have home fixtures.

Suppose most people asked to guess my secret ambition would come up with a century before lunch at Lord's or Trent Bridge or a place in the final of Mastermind. Well, they'd be wrong.

I dream of skipping the light fandango and waltzing the night away as a perfectly tailored ballroom dancer with the pick of the best partners in the business. All that glitter and glamour simply takes me by the hand when the music starts.

Sadly, I'm none too light on my feet, as various colleagues at the crease will testify after calling for a quick single. Tweaker Holmes went so far as to describe my antics as "living rigor mortis" with every run "a subject for lengthy negotiations."

A bit harsh. But perhaps I'm a few twirls away yet from a big night out with Ginger Rogers.

HAVE A GO

Evening classes organised by the WEA will be held in the village hall this autumn. Subjects include An Introduction to Local History, Elementary French, Watercolour Painting for Beginners and Romantic Novelists.

The Muckspreader, 1959

MOBILE LIBRARY

After many months of earnest negotiation, the County Council has finally agreed to include a mobile library visit to our village. It will call on the last Thursday of the month, parking opposite the school from 11am to 1pm. Parish councillor Harold Boldero, who led the campaign for the service, remarked: "This is a turn-up for the books".

The Muckspreader, 1957

TRUE SPIRIT

We have received a charming letter from our former Rector, the Rev Paul Hipperson, who left St Bartholomew's after 11 years to take up a new post in Kent.

"We were deeply moved by all sentiments expressed at our farewell social. Amy and the children join me in extending warmest thanks to our Rumoledew 'family' for their love and support over the years.

"I was particularly grateful for the parting gift of a bottle of choice cherries preserved in old brandy. Much appreciated as a handsome present... but appreciated even more for the spirit in which it was given."

The Muckspreader, 1960

RECIPE CORNER

It may be called brawn in other parts of the country, but Rumoledew stalwarts still serve up pork cheese. Thanks to Edith Trett for this simple but tasty recipe:

Collect a fresh hock from the butchers and boil for at least two hours. The meat leaves the bone to tell you it has cooked. Take saucepan off the heat and remove all bits of bone. Add pepper and salt to taste and a grating of nutmeg. Pour into a basin. Leave in cool place to set. Next day, tip it out of the basin and a nourishing pork cheese is ready to serve.

The Muckspreader, 1998

12

LIFTING THE LID

Linda Horton, niece of oldest resident Walter Grimes, runs the mother-and-toddler group in the village hall and performs several other roles in Rumoledew social life. She plays the piano for the annual pantomime fun.

With my own children flying the nest, I needed something to stop me sitting around and waiting to grow old. So I set up the mother-and-toddler club to keep in regular touch with tears, tantrums, toys and messy tea parties.

Then I go to the other end of the age scale and drop in to see Uncle Walter most days just to make sure he's ticking over nicely. A real old Norfolk character always ready to put the world to rights with his wit and wisdom.

I have taped quite a lot of his memories but there's plenty to come. "Hurry up, gal" he says, "dew I'll conk out afore we git ter the juicy bits behind the bike shed!" He never got married, but they tell me he had his moments.

I spend a fair bit of time down the village hall. This one was built to mark the new millennium, a truly modern job with a proper stage and lighting, kitchen, toilets, changing rooms and showers for the sports teams and plenty of parking space outside. Funny though how I still miss the old hall with its musty smell and wonky tables for whist drives, jumble sales and flower shows.

I met my husband Mick there at a youth club dance – he has two left feet, but a lovely smile – so I was bound to feel rather attracted to a survivor from another age. We try hard not to cling too closely to the past but you're tempted to start most sentences with "Now, when I was your age..." when youngsters start bleating about being bored 'cos there's nothing to do.

To be fair, they're not too bad round here although it only takes two or three the worse for wear after a night out in Norwich to send a shudder of apprehension through the village. Anti-social antics, shouting, swearing and tiddling over garden fences ,seem so much nastier at three in the morning.

When I hear "colourful" language from youngsters round the place, I do try the old trick of asking what their parents would think of such behaviour. Well, I know most of the families, or at least something about them, so there is a reasonable chance of a little bit of respect coming out of embarrassment.

Mind you, a good old-fashioned ding o' the lug from a good old-fashioned village policeman on a bike would be quicker and more effective. Perhaps he'll be back by the time our current toddlers start feeling their feet. Rumoledew could be in the vanguard of a social revolution to fully restore proper law and order to rural areas!

My regular contact with young mums does encourage me to take a wider view on occasions after making inevitable comparisons with how it used to be. We didn't have wall-to-wall television and mobile phones with all the gadgets. We were always out walking in and around the village and talking to each other and the children face-to-face. Communication was a simpler business in a smaller world.

Today's mothers seem to have much more to worry about at home, school and in the community. I tell them that's why they need each other more. Four of them got together recently to form The Bubbles (telly soaps a speciality) and take part in the pub quiz on Monday nights. They are also quite useful on pop music, fashion and celebrity television. I'm challenging them now to work on an act for the next village panto.

I take my hat off to Belinda Arthurton for the way she's breathed fresh life into our local entertainment. She gave me the posh title of "musical director" for the panto. I just play the piano and try to keep in time and tune with performers, many of them making their debuts on stage. Some are much worse than others – and they usually get the loudest cheers.

Time to take the lid off my little secret... and I blush with shame on letting down the family name. My mother, grand-mothers, aunts and sisters could all come up with the perfect Norfolk dumpling, fluffy, tasty and filling. I'm afraid mine are complete sinkers, stodgy, bland and unappetising.

Mick and Uncle Walter said they'd keep quiet about this dreadful gap in my culinary expertise if I stopped pretending it didn't exist. "You're good at everything else" they tell me, patting full stomachs and winking playfully. But I simply can't help making one more bid to rise above the mediocre.

I have consulted all family experts and old recipe books and even written to a couple of television chefs to see if they can help me beat the curse. One replied that is all a matter of flour power.

Mick did make me laugh the other Sunday when I tried yet again to build a lunch around "real" Norfolk dumplings. "They might not be up to much, my bewty," he mused. "But at least your gravy's moving about more freely."

WISH LIST FOR A NEW ERA

This final edition of The Muckspreader in the 20th century is pleased to bring results of the special survey conducted in our village over recent months.

A form was delivered to every household with an invitation to place in order of priority those things residents would most welcome at the start of a new millennium.

Over 100 forms were filled and returned for scrutiny by the parish council, so this "wish list" must be fairly representative of Rumoledew views.

"We have much new food for thought and we will do our utmost to follow all reasonable paths signposted by the people we try to serve" said parish council chairman Clifford Gaskin.

Here are the main items in order of votes cast:

- More affordable housing, especially for young
- Secure future for shop and post office
- Fundraising boost for St Bartholomew's repairs
- Revival of village football club
- Extra visits from community police patrols
- Monthly litter-picks around the village
- More helpers at youth club activities
- Better parking in all areas
- Stricter response to dog-fouling
- Annual real ale festival at The Four Ferrets.

The Muckspreader 1999

13

SOUND OF SILENCE

Dominic Hastings is one of several "part-timers" on the Rumoledew beat. He and partner Lisa work for a public relations firm based in London, often staying in the capital for days at a time before retuning to their rented village cottage.

We are honoured guests of this fine old rural parish – but some guests, it seems, are more welcome than others. "You just use the place as a convenience" hinted a local stalwart on one of our weekend outings to The Four Ferrets.

As were not exchanging idle banter in the pub toilet at the time, I took this remark as a thinly-disguised throwback to the sort of welcome usually reserved for pillaging Danes and plundering Vikings in the good old days. Biggest difference, of course, is that we spend good money in the pub while these earlier invaders would have set light to it.

The cottage we rent used to be home to a farm labourer and his family. Well, they are pretty thin on the ground nowadays and my inquiries suggest they wouldn't feel too comfortable in any case with a "colour supplement" conversion. So people like us help them plead "not guilty" in the great debate about exploitation of our precious countryside.

Perhaps it's us who are being ripped off by estate agents, lured to gentle backwaters by bucolic images and the sound of silence only to discover an ethnic minority of remarkable sophistication and ceaseless conversation.

I exaggerate, of course, bur far too much is being made of a supposed gap between hardworking commuters bright enough to want a country retreat and suspicious natives who think London is only meant for Coronations, Cup Finals, Cockney capers – and underworld crooks.

I carry no qualms over this sort of dual citizenship. Our work in London, all complicated orders and deadlines, is only occasionally exciting but constantly exacting. It's lovely to leave it behind and escape to the simple life in a Norfolk community. We don't so much switch off as pull out the plug, turn off at the mains and sit round the candle of rural charm.

I've told our hard-boiled critics that there's nothing to stop them getting their own back and piling into the capital to exercise fertility rites in and around Piccadilly Circus. Just modify those Norfolk accents and leave the tractors behind - and no-one will notice any difference.

In some ways Norfolk's proud insularity comes as a surprise, despite its geographical position sticking out into the North Sea. It has been invaded throughout history by well-meaning missionaries wading ashore while a vast network of rural railway lines must have attracted a few more helpful strangers.

Then came all those Americans when they realised there was a war on. Aerodromes sprang up all over Norfolk and young men from Texas and Maine were introduced to seasoned sugar beet workers as they set out along more endless rows.

In more recent times, overspill brought London voices and London ways to the likes of Thetford and King's Lynn. Polish and Portuguese workers arrived, many of them to pick and sort out fruit and vegetables, and the European Economic Community is bound to exert more influences in years to come.

Surely a few grateful commuters can be absorbed into a settlement like Rumoledew. Who knows, we could learn how to breed, and talk properly and eventually outnumber the old guard. Then we can tear up our rail season tickets, turn all barns into IT centres and PR offices... and build a real drawbridge to keep out interlopers.

I wasn't born in Norfolk but one of my great-aunts was evacuated to the county during the war and my eldest sister once went out with a chap from Fakenham. (They met on a murder mystery weekend in Basingstoke. He'd clearly followed the wrong clues.)

So when I attract subtle observations like "You're not from around here, are you?", I play up my proud local connections and throw in a useful impersonation of the Singing Postman letting rip with "Hev Yew Gotta Loight, Boy?" It usually buys me a bit of quality time in the pub.

We may settle here full-time one day as long as we can get through passport control with our forged naturalisation papers. Then I'll be able to pursue my green dream and grow all our own vegetables on a Rumoledew allotment, complete with scarecrow and garden shed.

My other big ambition, kept under wraps for obvious reasons, is to propose to Lisa in the middle of a freshly-harvested field on a moonlight night, mouth the traditional local incantation "Hubble, bubble, toil and stubble", and then seek permission to marry in St Bartholomew's before Advent.

Surely that would be enough to soften the hardest Norfolk heart, and earn us a handy discount on a full house for our reception at The Four Ferrets.

We would, of course, have to charge locals for all drinks.

CHAPEL MEMORIES
WANTED FOR BOOK

Following the closure of Rumoledew Methodist Chapel after 127 years, Harold Boldero is planning to compile a book of memories about the building and characters and events connected with it.

"My own family links go back to the early 1900s, and I remember some colourful preachers who graced the pulpit when I was a boy. Men like 'Thumper' Green and 'Sniffer' Hargreaves" said Harold.

"We gave them nicknames which have stuck over the years. 'Thumper' used to bang on the pulpit to emphasise a point and keep the congregation alert while 'Sniffer' held the hymn book very close to his face, almost sniffing it, because of poor eyesight."

Sunday School outings, anniversaries and harvest festivals are on Mr Boldero's list for special chapters if sufficient memories and photographs are forthcoming.

Please contact him if you can help at "Bethel", Back Lane, Rumoledew.

The Muckspreader, 1989

14
CLOSE TO NATURE

Dilly Harcourt-Lyte is into herbal remedies and fortune-telling, cutting a colourful figure as she cycles round the village in flowery floral dress, straw hat and sandals. Her "hippy" image disguises a distinguished academic past.

It's hardly surprising that I've reached the dizzy heights of being called "The Witch of Rumoledew" through my passionate belief in unconventional methods.

My father was a family doctor in rural Somerset at a time when country remedies, freely available from field and hedge, were an integral part of life. My mother could read palms and faces in a way no-one could deny she had "the gift". I studied botany at Oxford University and spent several years on special research into herbalism.

Put all those ingredients together and you get a happy soul still seeking enlightenment in a part of the country where showing faith in nature does not automatically mean a one-way ticket to the funny farm! Even so, it was a bit of an accident as to how I arrived.

I used to visit an aunt in Southwold for summer breaks in the late 1950s when she constantly warned me against straying over the border into Norfolk "where they eat their young and play 'I Spy with my middle eye'..." Of course, that whetted my appetite to take a look at this strange land full of superstition and strange antics.

A reunion with a couple of cousins on holiday in Wroxham about eight years ago brought me back to the county and reawakened an old urge to settle in a quiet village. A bungalow with a patch of land near the old railway halt came on the market while I was out scouting in the areas – and so Comfrey Corner, as I called it, persuaded me to totally ignore Aunt Althea's advice.

My passport to local acceptance was stamped by an appearance as Madame Moonlight at the church fete. I did a roaring trade telling fortunes although I had been here long enough to know where a little economy with the more dramatic forecasts might come in useful. Sure enough, certain characters are at the front of the queue when I hold fresh sessions under canvas.

It's strange how some people revel in the prospect of calamity on the horizon – "I told my old man that would happen if he didn't alter his ways!" – while others are reluctant to go until they have been offered a glimmer of hope. Country customers are far more phlegmatic about fate than their urban counterparts.

I soon realised this was fertile ground for folk remedies, some of which have been added to my extensive collection. One old boy, since moved on to even more verdant acres, insisted his recipe for a long and healthy Rumoledew life was based on "Keep your bowels open, your pecker up and your faith in the Lord!"

He also swore by cabbage water and nettle tea for purifying

the blood and liquorice powder for purifying the system. His remedy for rheumatism, two or three drops of oil of juniper on a lump of sugar in the morning, works for me.

Many of these alternative medicines have been passed down through several generations, and I'm delighted to report strong interest among several young mothers in the village. For all that, I'm having trouble in convincing them a dock leaf and fresh cowpat can still work wonders!

Despite the "witch" label, meant, I'm sure, as more of a compliment than a criticism, I feel quite at home among people unafraid to take from the past if it helps make a little more sense of modern life. I can walk or cycle quiet lanes to gather free medicines, natural antidotes with proven virtues. I can recommend feverfew as an excellent cure for migraine, fully aware that it used to be the top remedy for the ague, a type of malaria at one time too prevalent in the Fens.

While I can't tell my own fortune with any degree of reassuring accuracy, I suspect this will be my final staging post before I find a heavenly respite from all earthly ills.

I don't have many ambitions left at my time of life apart from continued good health and an inquiring mind. But I'd love to get the invitation to present a television programme about plants and treatment of ailments.

I'd call it Country Cures, showing how domestic plant remedies might become extinct, only to be replaced by "official" herbalism as a part of the back-to-nature movement.

Many people are worried about undesirable side effects of many drugs used in modern medicine. That's one of the main reasons behind the upsurge of interest in all forms of alternative medicine.

Frankly, I'm very surprised it hasn't been done already on a large scale with regular national exposure. Perhaps the biggest barrier in the way of small-screen stardom for me, fading good looks aside, would be an unshakeable insistence on talking proper English throughout.

I may collect the odd plant from a level playing field. But, y'know, at this moment in time, at the end of the day, I have to tick all the right seed boxes nestling on the window of opportunity....

Okay, that's a worse-case scenario when all is said and done. But you can see where I'm coming from.

NATURE NOTES
by Wanderer

The fields, lanes and woods around Rumoledew are alive with the glories of autumn.

In many places mushrooms and blackberries are at their best at the gentle tail end of September. Garden spiders are busy building large webs which sparkle when the morning dew collects in droplets on them.

Conkers and horse chestnut leaves will soon start tumbling together to produce that rich, musty aroma of autumn. Crackling leaves at the foot of hedges are full of life as slugs and snails saunter down from the branches.

Blackbirds fill themselves almost to bursting on fallen apples. Robins and wrens spearhead a brief but beautiful autumn chorus. Hedge sparrows that have spent the day alone call winsomely to each other at dusk and often roost in pairs.

The Muckspreader, 1977

15

YOUNG OUTLOOK

Jason Gladwell, 19, is one of very few home-grown youngsters able to stay close to his roots on leaving school. He lives with his parents in the village and works as a mechanic at the garage near the crossroads. But he knows his days as a Rumoledew resident could be numbered

I don't know what all the others have been saying about the village but my views are bound to be a bit different because I'm fairly young and fairly ambitious.

My dad reckons most people my age "don't know they're born". I think he means we're very lucky to have such caring and generous parents protecting us from the horrors of the real world. Well, he's never worked or lived anywhere else – so how come he's an expert on what we're missing?

There are two more after me in our house, brother Simon, who is 16 and sister Cheryl, nearly 13. They want to go on to college or university to get more qualifications. I left school as soon as they'd let me out and went straight to work for Mr Crisp at the garage.

I always wanted to be a mechanic and would hang around the place after school and at weekends till they found me little jobs to do with oil cans and spanners. Dad's a keen cricketer and asked me to practise hard and join him in the club. But that takes up too much time, especially now I'm going out seriously with Carol.

We hope to get engaged soon and start looking round for somewhere to live. She's a hairdresser, so our wages together don't add up to nearly enough to think about staying in Rumoledew. This business about "affordable housing" in rural areas is a right joke – and I don't think my parents will want to put up with both of us as "paying guests".

I don't want to leave the village but there won't be much choice if we decide to set up home. Maybe we could rent a flat in the town or city and I'd have to get another garage job closer by. Carol says she'll do what's best for us.

We hear a lot from politicians at all levels about how sad it is to see so many young people forced away from their country roots by a shortage of jobs and ridiculous house prices. That's been going on since before I was born – and still they keep building executive dwellings when there's any building at all.

I reckon Rumoledew will finish up full of rich retired incomers and highly-paid commuters keen to get away from the rat race when it suits them. That should keep property prices well out of the reach of my generation and the one to follow.

My Dad and his old man before him worked on the land for a pittance and lived in tied cottages. To be honest, they didn't have any choice but to stay in the village and raise families. Dad had to find another job as a delivery van driver when the farm laid him off. At least he couldn't tell me to go knockin' and toppin' sugar beet like his father told him.

"An era has ended, boy, but people will still want to live in small places where they feel they belong" he reminded me when I left school and started paying a few quid towards my keep. Yes, so they might, but that list will be restricted to them what can afford it. Simple as that.

He calls me a "cheeky young warmint" when I come out with a few home truths, but Mum says I'm right to sum up the situation honestly. If I want a garage of my own one day, first thing is to realise the streets of Rumoledew are not paved with gold. Better wages and more opportunities are waiting for anyone ready to show a bit of courage.

In the meantime, I have to save up for a proper car by being nice and helpful to locals who don't have much idea about looking after one. I could cry at some of the cruel treatment dished out.

Perhaps I'm a bit young to have much of a shady past but I can own up to one of two pranks on the school bus during my last year.

I let the frogs out of the basket at the back that morning when the driver threatened to report us to the county education committee for cruelty to wildlife. I told him it was a controlled biology experiment in an enclosed environment and was part of our homework.

The real reason was to scare the girls so much they would shriek and cling to boys who would protect them best. My relationship with Carol moved on leaps and bounds.

I was also responsible for adding a scarecrow, or a "mawkin" as Dad calls it, to our back-seat ranks after telling the driver it was needed for the school pantomime In fact, we left it on the bus for him to look after till going-home time.

Now, I've already admitted I would love to have my own

garage to run, even welcoming harassed school bus drivers, but there's another big wish on my list.

How I'd love to be a stunt driver in a James Bond film or something like that to earn enough money to buy the biggest old house in Rumoledew!

For now, I'll have a word with my best mate Barrie and find out how you get into stock-car racing at Yarmouth. Reckon you might need a few frogs on the back to get things bouncing.

FANCY DRESS WINNERS

We asked for memories of 1953 Coronation celebrations in the village. Such has been the response that it will take several editions to feature them all. Please be patient!

Let's start with the fancy dress competition which attracted nearly 30 entries after tea in the village hall.

Here are the winners, Alice and the White Rabbit, as portrayed by sisters Linda and Veronica Booth. "We won a shilling each as well as boxes of crayons and colouring books" recalls Linda.

She thinks a jockey came in second and a milkmaid third. "There were a few tears from Simple Simon, who stalked off the stage with his pies – and went home before the final parade."

The Muckspreader, 1977

16
MUCKING IN

Helen Keymer and her husband Eric were among the first arrivals at The Pastures, a pleasantly-spread settlement of "executive" houses in the village. She acknowledges it can be tough finding full acceptance in a fresh environment.

The first thing I'm going to do is refuse to apologise for finding and settling in this lovely part of Norfolk. We spent many happy holidays in the county before deciding to move here permanently.

Yes, we could afford one of those smart new houses at the height of the property boom as Eric prepared to retire from his post of managing director of a small engineering firm in Basildon. But our decision was based on genuine affection for the area and a real desire to involve ourselves in the community.

Eric had to take it gently after a heart attack scare but I have tried to "muck in" wherever possible, joining the parish council, local Women's Institute and organising keep-fit classes – "the

Keymer Therapists" as Eric calls us – at the village hall. There's no time to sit about nursing regrets.

Life on the parish council was testing to say the least during my first few months as home-grown defenders of grass-roots democracy suspected I was there to preach an Essex expansionist gospel. To some, I represented the unacceptable face of "posh and rich incomers who move in and want to take over."

I think I've convinced all but the most dogmatic that my motives are pure and simple, to do what I can to help Rumoledew continue along its homely way. People like us don't move into a small rural village to call for wholesale changes.

We may not have enjoyed the privilege of being born and raised here, but we shouldn't be condemned automatically for showing belated good taste.

I saw enough of my home county of Essex covered with concrete to appreciate how special much of Norfolk remains. There's no reason why newcomers shouldn't play an important part in maintaining those special qualities.

My proudest moment here so far came when a village elder thanked me publicly at a council meeting for reminding the true locals what we are all fighting for. I think it was a compliment.

Eric, born in Northampton, raised in Kettering and educated mostly in Chelmsford before embarking on his engineering career in Corby and Basildon, says it's good to start putting down proper roots at his time of life. Probably the first chance he's had to think about belonging to a certain place.

He thinks seriously about these matters and advised me to tread very carefully at early parish council meetings and other local gatherings where they weigh you up.

"Listen, smile, agree and ask if they've got any eggs or vegetables for sale. You'll find out all about them without really trying. Then you can take the initiative next time because there'll be a bit of common ground."

Eric, who reads folk very well, reckons there's a Rumoledew rump determined to keep the UDI flag waving deep into the 21st century. "They see it as a mark of progress to disagree with newcomers after years of simply falling out with each other. It's a new kind of feudalism, with them pulling on the peasant's smock and us in the role of greedy landlord or wicked squire."

There's still a bit of a divide between The Pastures and the "old" village but that can generate a whiff of healthy competition when it comes to pub quiz rounds and annual events like the flower and vegetable show.

We hired a good old boy from Tanner Lane to look after our garden shortly after arriving. Our tulips and runner beans won runners-up certificates that summer – and Tom immediately decided to take "early retirement" at 82. We couldn't prove anything of course, but it was widely rumoured that he'd been warned off by those who usually won all the prizes.

I've always been a keep-fit enthusiast, playing badminton and tennis regularly, and so it was no hardship to organise weekly sessions here to fight the flab and oil the joints. There was a fair bit of puffing and creaking when we first got together on Monday afternoons but I like to think all those who kept going have benefitted.

There's talk of a rambling group being set up soon – and I assume that has nothing to do with the way some Norfolk people hold court when anyone will listen.

Now for a little something about me that won't be generally known, but I have the photographs and newspaper cuttings to prove it. I was Basildon Carnival Queen in 1973 – and that's how I met Eric.

He was chairman of the local chamber of trade and one of the judges. We married two years later and spent part of our honeymoon on the Norfolk Broads.

That was the start of our love affair with a wonderful county.

"HYMNATHON" FOR TOWER APPEAL

Our new Rector, the Rev Kevin Barton, has lost no time in squaring up to big challenges at St Bartholomew's.

Initial work on restoring the church tower is estimated to cost about £70,000 and while some grants may be available parishioners are being urged to come up with as many fundraising ideas as possible.

A "hymnathon" will be staged in the church as part of the June Flower Festival with exhibitors and supporters encouraged to join a marathon hymn-singing session on the Saturday from dawn to dusk. Sponsors are being sought, both individually and from clubs, organisations and local businesses.

An antiques road show in the village hall, a comic football match between men and women dressed as the opposite sex and a family talent show are other proposals under consideration.

The Muckspreader, 2007

WHATEVER NEXT?

Overheard at a recent parish council meeting: "They move in, take over – and then want to take the amendment first."

The Muckspreader, 1993

17

PROMISED LAND

Mike Boldero has a finger in most Rumoledew village pies. He is immensely proud of his Norfolk roots and accent and is a widely acknowledged expert on the local dialect. Parish councillor, actor, writer, quiz master and reliable handyman... he's already a village legend.

I wanted to write my impressions in Broad Norfolk until a still, small voice in my lug proffered a reminder that we are now a proudly cosmopolitan community.

Some would say that's posh for being taken over by newcomers – but while we remain in the majority, and therefore able to carry on operating as prophets in our own country, we must temper parochial passion with all-embracing benevolence.

I like to think of us as the Norfolk Home Guard, defending celery trenches and back garden shelters against the jackboot of turgid uniformity. Well, it gives us something useful to do while potential new recruits whine on about all the remarkable things they've left behind.

It can be both stimulating and fun trying to convince incomers how fortunate they are to have finished up in the Promised Land, even if a few soon discover they like neither milk nor honey (And they thought both were available only from a supermarket).

It's when people on either side lose their sense of humour that the whole business degenerates into a nasty shouting match – "Go back where you came from!" versus "That's what inbreeding does for you!"

Norfolk fundamentalists can laugh at themselves, but they don't like being derided for possessing the good sense to stay in the same place because it happens to be the sensible thing. "I haven't lived or worked anywhere else" should be treated as a proud boast, not a contrite apology.

Villages like ours have always thrived on a swig or two of well-brewed animosity. My father, a highly-respected Methodist local preacher for over 30 years, was none too charitable towards "furriners" who moved in and tried to impose changes "just for the sake of it".

You could count the number of newcomers on one hand in those years just after the last war, but he would have set them a written and oral entrance examination if rules allowed. "They're all God's people" mother would suggest quietly. "Well, why doesn't He send them where they'd be appreciated?" came the standard reply.

Now we have the pub quiz to keep the pot boiling. I'm one of the regular question masters, a position which carries a privilege of waving the Norfolk flag with relish. It evens things out a bit when the locals are up against a brainy bunch of well-travelled, university-educated, Guardian-reading refugees from the Mastermind studio.

It's lovely to watch them squirm and look at each other in utter bewilderment when asked where Shannocks come from or what you would do with a hutkin. A recent tie-breaker about the "Muddle and Get Nowhere" railway line proved to be the signal for accusations of bias in favour of certain contestants.

In fact, it's nothing more than nudging local culture into the limelight. And if I moved to, say, Coventry or Rochdale, I'd brush up on Lady Godiva and Gracie Fields. There's nothing wrong with local pride ... even it if does take an inordinately long time to qualify for the "local" tag. General estimates still put the settling-in period at between 15 and 20 years.

Sensible folk can make a reasonable pitch within a fortnight if they take the trouble to listen, look and learn before commenting favourably on the status quo. Save criticisms for the second year – and then make sure they stand up to proper scrutiny in the pub.

I don't pretend this place is idyllic. There are pockets of real poverty, mental health and drugs problems and anti-social behaviour. It is small and knit together enough, however, to know where the difficulties are and what's needed to tackle them.

My handyman rounds, painting, mending, gardening and mardling, opens doors all round the village and beyond to give me a fair idea what's going on, what's worrying people and where the parish council should stick controversial planning applications.

I pick up plenty of raw material for the annual pantomime script, and most folk in our sell-out audiences are there to make sure I've included their special lines. A sort of cultural co-operative without an Arts Council grant.

My Norfolk rural life is a fairly open book, even if a few

pages are turned down at the corners, while having a preacher for a father tended to encourage village elders to keep a beady eye on all my antics. Other boys got away with risky adventures as I tried to live up to the family's goo d name.

My one big fall from grace, pricking my conscience for so many years, came at the Coronation sports of 1953. I'm ashamed to admit that I used chewing gum to help me win the 100 yards egg-and-spoon race and a shiny new sixpence.

I still have that coin in my bedside cabinet, reminding me to stick to proper principles on life's tough circuit.

SHOW YOU CARE

Careful scrutiny of parish council minutes for the past few years proves certain topics get more than their fair share of airings.

Blocked rights of way, dog fouling on the playing field, dumping of household rubbish, thoughtless parking outside houses on Back Lane, vandalism at the village hall and a tendency to be completely ignored by other councils further up the local government ladder head the list.

Now comes the chance for residents to be positive and optimistic and to show some real pride in their community. Designs for a new village sign are being invited while consideration is being given to a proposal that Rumoledew should apply to become a conservation area.

Please take your considered views to the October meeting and show you care.

The Muckspreader, 2009

18

FARMYARD FRESH

Beth Willgress lives and works at Holly Farm with husband Nigel and three children. She runs a flourishing "farm stay" holiday business for a growing number of folk who like a break in the heart of the county.

It was Nigel's father who issued a stark warning when he retired from the farm 15 years ago – "diversify or die." A bit dramatic, just like the old boy as he railed against all the red tape unfurled by the blessed Common Agricultural Policy, but we took the hint.

Nigel decided to get out of dairy farming shortly after taking over and that left several outbuildings going spare. We checked carefully with others who had taken the plunge and decided to follow the trend and offer holiday accommodation.

Conversion work was costly and there were times when we wondered if bankruptcy might kill off our plans. But that cussed Norfolk streak, plus practical support from all the family, brought Farmyard Fresh Breaks into being. Now business is booming – and I tell Nigel he's a kept farmer!

Holidaymakers adore the idea of sleeping and eating in the old cowshed or dairy and there's a network of bridle paths around Holly Farm where they can walk off bumper breakfasts. It's a lovely area for birdwatching and spotting wildlife and there's also a chance to see how a real farm works.

My sister Mandy helps out during the peak summer season when we get several families, most of them eager to taste country life for the first time. Dear old Walter Grimes, who worked on the farm for 50 years, drops in regularly to tell visitors about "them hard old days" of long hours and meagre wages.

He does lay it on a bit thick and makes Nigel's predecessors sound like slave-drivers – but the twinkle in his eye always suggests he's spicing up the yarns.

Our children love getting involved with the visitors, especially when they can help with serving meals. Amy's motives may be mercenary as she collects useful tips from the table, but her reputation as a budding showjumper does depend on useful income to supplement our considerable outlay.

Nigel has organised a few farm tours for families keen to know more about livestock, husbandry and crop rotation, although his time for such exploits is rather limited. "I'm not a gentleman farmer lording it over a large workforce" he insists. "I am the workforce."

Will our boys take over one day? Well, both Henry and Mark lap up the outside life, but it might be a bit different if they had to crawl out of bed on a frosty night to sort out a sick bullock or a ewe having trouble giving birth. To be fair, Nigel has warned them not to get too romantic about life down on the farm.

We try to keep in regular touch with village activities. I was persuaded to join the WI as part of the "young blood" campaign launched a couple of years ago, and Nigel had his arm twisted to become vice-chairman of the village hall and playing field committee. A shredded ligament ended his playing days but he's still passionate about sport.

He is aware of the family tradition going back four generations at Holly Farm and its part in the village "establishment". Even so, he reckons simple economics will change the face of the local landscape even more dramatically in the next half-century or so.

Entertaining people from town and city might well encourage the better-off to embrace full-time country life, but that's bound to pile extra pressure on housing resources for youngsters born in the village and anxious to stay there. And where will the jobs come from? Nigel's father and grandfather employed dozens of men and women during their years at the helm. Nigel mostly works alone.

Although I have a good Norfolk pedigree, with my parents running a farm near Downham Market, I'm still serving my Rumoledew apprenticeship. This remains a tight-knit village and changing my name to Willgress did help make my arrival reasonably painless.

But some with deep roots are quick to remind me that mine have a long way to go when there's a discussion about village affairs. "Of course, you weren't born here, were you?" can sound like the most serious of accusations.

Although my days of dreaming about being a ballet dancer are long gone, I do cherish an ambition to perform my own version of Swan Lake as a cultural interlude during the annual pantomime. The children have said they would die of shame. Nigel reckons it would be grounds for divorce.

As for something serious about me that could well shock the

populace at large outside Farmyard Fresh Breaks, I offer a disciplinary record bordering on the criminal during my boarding school days in Suffolk.

I was dismissed from lacrosse and hockey matches for "unladylike antics and language" and dropped from the netball team for questioning Miss Carpenter's use of the whistle at crucial times and her general interpretation of the rulebook

She vehemently denied the need to see an optician – and sent me to see the headmistress. We agreed it would be best if I spent Wednesday afternoons far from the sporting crowd.

TAKE CARE

As local roads groan under the extra burden of holiday traffic, mainly heading for the coast, we commend these lines to all Rumoledew drivers:

You watch the guy who drives ahead
And the guy who drives behind
You watch the left and watch the right
And drive with a calm, clear mind
But the guy you really have to watch
On the highway you will find
Is the guy behind the guy ahead
And ahead of the guy behind.
                    The Muckspreader, 1983

19
FAITH RESTORED

Harry Benbow retired with his wife Ena to Clover Cottage on the out-
skirts of the village after a 30-year career in the Metropolitan Police.
"Paradise after purgatory... but I had to earn the money to afford it.
That's the way of the world. Case closed" he said on arrival.

Like thousands of other lucky couples, we found Norfolk through the holiday brochures. It was too easy to put it on top of our list of retirement locations after three summer breaks on the North Norfolk coast.

You have to live and work in London long enough to fully appreciate the need for somewhere else to restore your faith in human nature. My years as a copper, rising to the rank of Detective Inspector, made me cynical, sad and exhausted... although I did enjoy putting a few choice villains away.

At times, you find yourself dealing with pure evil. So it's no hardship to wake up, open the window and realise the biggest trouble of the day could be stopping bluetits pecking milk bottle tops on the doorstep.

Hard to believe we're in the same country, only about 100 miles from the capital. We give thanks every morning for this remarkable contrast and wonder how long it'll be before we join the drawbridge brigade. After all, it is very tempting to want to keep this sort of haven of tranquillity to yourselves.

Still, old habits die hard and I know how appearances can be deceptive after watching butter-wouldn't-melt-in-their-mouths characters revealed as brutal murderers. And why do you think so many detective stories are set in pretty rural refuges?

I'm not suggesting Miss Marple would have a field day in Rumoledew as the vicar calls and teacups clink, but crime is not a complete stranger along these leafy lanes.

Most of the idle gossip wouldn't stand up as evidence in a court but some of the character references might encourage the judge to put on his black cap. I'm amazed at the way people talk so openly about their neighbours, even their relatives. I'm even more amazed at so few cases of justifiable retribution.

Then there are quiz sessions worth of scrutiny by the Director of Public Prosecutions if he can spare a night at The Four Ferrets. Questions loaded in favour of home-grown con-testants could yet spark race riots or an independent tribunal. How on earth can a chap from London know the two Norfolk villages with only three letters?

Natives can't take all the blame for upsetting images in front of houses new and old. Plastic gnomes with fishing rods ought to be taken in for serious questioning – it's probably still an offence to drown them in artificial ponds – while concrete angels and animals ought to stand accused of forming a riotous assembly.

Talking of the parish council, I decided to stay out of the

firing line until locals drop their slightly facetious description of me as "Benbow of the Yard".

That should ensure a quiet life for at least 20 years.....

We enjoy an occasional meal at the pub and Ena has joined the flower arranging rota at the church. I may be cajoled into taking part in the next village pantomime with a song or two from my Gilbert and Sullivan repertoire. Mustn't let the voice get too rusty.

My big aim is to help set up a local history society with outings, talks, a newsletter and social events to encourage useful membership. Only problem is that the person who suggests such an organisation is very likely to be lumbered with the role of chairman.

I made the mistake of volunteering once for the police social club committee – and it took nearly all my career to find a way out.

It took a lot of soul searching to bring to the surface something about me that our freshly-adopted friends wouldn't know or even guess. A senior policeman's book is an open one for anybody who cares to turn the pages, and I did figure in several high-profile cases which attracted national publicity.

My "confession" goes back to boyhood days in Poplar, where I was born and lived until I left school to become a police cadet. Returning home from youth club one Friday night in winter, I took a chance on riding my bike without lights.

Out of the shadows, just round the corner after the church stepped PC Larkins in all his caped glory. He put up a hand to stop me breaking the law – but he wasn't quite strong enough.

My front wheel caught his right shin. I caught a right earful of colourful language as I went sprawling over the pavement. My injuries were far worse than his, but that didn't prevent a lengthy lecture before he picked up me and machine and sent us on our way.

He told me years later when I joined the force how close he'd come to putting a big spoke in my wheel of ambition.

IT'S A CLASS REUNION

The first official village school reunion proved a big success with over 70 former pupils answering the register in the main classroom.

The event, organised by Linda Horton and Mike Boldero, attracted old boys and girls from as far away as Leeds, London, Hastings and Swansea.

There was a special welcome for Edward Wight, a nephew of Miss Emma Langley, headteacher at the school from 1936 until her retirement in 1962. Mr Wight, a barrister based in London, was a regular visitor to the village during his aunt's time at the school. Several of her former pupils attended the

Miss Emma Langley and her pet dog Coleridge. Miss Langley was headteacher at Rumoledew from 1936 until 1962.

reunion and spoke fondly of her firm but fair authority.

Old attendance books and photographs sparked a stream of memories throughout the evening which ended with a buffet and a vote of thanks to all concerned from Mike Boldero.

Another reunion is likely to be staged in two years' time.

The Muckspreader, 1996

20
PRODIGAL DAUGHTER

Judy Hetherington is a single mother living with her parents in an extended bungalow near the school. She is caretaker at the village hall and regular cleaner of the office at the pallet-making business close to the old railway station.

People say they never see me without a duster or a brush in my hand and I have to admit I enjoy making things tidy and bright. Unfortunately, life isn't always like that however hard you try.

It's no secret in the village that I went off the rails after leaving school and moving away to find work and a bit of adventure. Then, as Dad put it, the "prodigal daughter returned" with more than she'd bargained for.

Mother reminded me what used to happen to unmarried mothers in small communities – and then set about trying to make life as comfortable as possible for me and Jess. She's settled nicely at the village school while I find plenty to keep me busy with two cleaning jobs.

CONFESSIONAL BOX
Emily Maitland

One of Rumoledew's top culinary experts is the latest "victim" to enter our Confessional Box where leading local personalities are encouraged to cook up straight answers to straight questions.

Emily Maitland's prizewinning flans have been a tasty feature of village cricket teas for many a season while her all-round flair in the kitchen makes her a big favourite at any local function where refreshments are on offer.

What started your rise to baking prominence? My mother and grandmother were wonderful cooks, both of them using wall ovens to make their own bread. It seemed only right to keep a proud family tradition going.

How do you make Norfolk dumplings? I use self-raising flour, a pinch of salt, a teaspoonful of baking powder and water to make a firm dough. Mix ingredients together and separate into four portions and roll into balls. Steam for 20 minutes. They can either be put on top of the potatoes to cook or placed on top of soup.

Do you have a favourite recipe? My flans always go down very well, but I also love making Norfolk shortcakes and treacle tart. My husband's favourite is marrow custard.

Are there too many cookery programmes on television? Yes, because that means fewer folk in the kitchen trying things for themselves. I picked up everything I know from watching my mother and grandmother and they told me to keep going till I got it right.

Your biggest kitchen disaster? Forgetting to put onions in a large bowl of onion soup.

Do you have any big faults? I can get irritable if I'm not cooking and I don't have many other topics of conversation. When my husband and family take me out for a meal they insist I don't give a running commentary on the menu.

What would you change in the village? Some attitudes towards healthy eating. It should be top priority for every family.

How would you like to be remembered? As a Norfolk mawther who dished up plenty of food for thought.

Thanks, Emily... you deserve your flan club!

The Muckspreader, 2007

As an only child, I'm fully aware how much of a disappointment I must have seemed to my parents. They are quiet, unassuming country folk with a clear understanding of what' right and what's wrong. I hurt them badly, especially when talk of taking drugs and excessive drinking on my part started to reach their friends.

They were confused and embarrassed by what appeared to be happening to an intelligent daughter who did well enough at school despite a lazy streak and gave no clues that she could fall into bad company.

Well, as I admitted later, village life for a teenager can be so frustrating and boring. You can't tell your parents how fed up you are because it reflects on them but school chums keep dropping big hints about all the fun you're missing.

I had no-one to talk to comfortably about such matters at home and so in the end I went down a path without really knowing where it might lead. All fun and excitement at first as you taste freedom, but life without certainties, like old-fashioned parents and your own thinking room, can turn you dizzy and daft

By the time it all got out of control and I fell pregnant I was too ashamed to drop a postcard to the old homestead and ask for my old life back. Eventually, with the help of a social worker and a good friend of my mother's I stood on the doorstep of "Headlands" with Jess in my arms.

Since that touching scene from a Victorian melodrama played out on a warm spring morning, we've all had to come to terms with dramatic changes in our small world. I think my parents have just about forgiven me while I've never noticed any open hostility towards me or my child in the village.

Perhaps the fact I've never tried to hide the truth has helped.

I'm a Norfolk girl who made a mistake and went home to try and rectify it. My roles as village hall caretaker and cleaner at the pallet-making business office help pay for our keep – and give me a worthwhile character reference.

I don't expect my parents to shoulder the blame for my fall from grace but there are lessons to be taken from the inescapable truth that we didn't talk enough to each other.

Yes, teenagers can be sulky and difficult, turning the generation gap into a chasm with moody silence or a sudden tantrum, but an honest mardle can work wonders.

A small offering, I know, but I do keep an eye open for troubled faces at the end of village hall functions. A quiet word of encouragement in a young ear shows someone cares. That's just as important in a small community as anywhere else.

"Dick" Barton, our smashing vicar, reckons my "evangelical zeal" on behalf of my fellow human beings should lead to some sort of post at St Bartholomew's, but I think that may be a step too far at this stage of my Rumoledew rehabilitation!

I enjoy going to church and helping with fundraising activities. Mother's jam sponges and fluffy scones make it impossible for me to go anywhere near the refreshments committee for fear of comparisons being made. It's a family curse I'm quite prepared to live with.

With my past inspected more closely than most, in a tight-knit village like this, I'm drawn easily to hopes and dreams for the future. I would like to find the right man, get married and enjoy a "proper" family life. At least my cleaning credentials are useful!

My other main ambition is to achieve something big enough to make my parents and daughter really proud and bring me a sense of satisfaction to wipe away bitter memories of the "lost" years.

Only a fanciful idea at the moment, but I intend to pursue inquiries about the Open University and what's involved in going for a degree in social work.

I know how support from a stranger lifted me up when I needed it most and made it possible to return where I belong.

THE RECTOR REFLECTS

We must all make our talents count in these difficult times.

I am reminded of a young clergyman, fresh out of training, who wanted to understand some of the fears and temptations his future congregations might face. So he took the job of a policeman.

He passed the physical. Then came the oral examination to test his ability to act quickly and wisely in an emergency.

Among other questions he was asked: "What would you do to disperse a frenzied crowd?" He thought for a moment and then replied: "I would pass round the collection plate."

He got the job.

The Muckspreader, 1972

CLOSE DECISION

From a parish magazine in another Norfolk community: "We are pleased to note that there has been a change of mind by the Housing Department regarding a name for our new housing complex for the elderly. 'St Peter's Close' did seem rather inappropriate."

The Muckspreader, 1979

CARD SCHOOL

This intriguing old photograph came to light during a recent house-clearing operation in the village.

The man seated on the left is thought to be Barnabas Leggett, landlord of The Four Ferrets pub before the First World War. If that is the case, this card school could well have been taking place at his Rumoledew establishment.

We will be delighted to receive any further details in time for the next edition.

The Muckspreader, 1974

HOUSEHOLD HINTS

Pine kitchen tables, properly left unvarnished, do require an occasional scrub. Take this example from housewives of the past, using one spoon of lime, two spoons of soap powder and three spoons of silver sand. A little should be sprinkled on the table top which is then scrubbed soundly with a scrubbing brush. Rinse with clean water and dry carefully.

The Muckspreader, 1956

21

CLEANING UP ROOTS

Local history enthusiasts in Rumoledew and the immediate area savoured a memorable treat on a cool but inviting September evening in 1986. A passionate talk by WEA lecturer Pete Diggins in a crowded Rumoledew Village Hall set the stage for an eight-week course, Cleaning Up Your Roots.

There may be some credence in claims that a few members of his audience arrived in expectation of signing up for evening classes all about gardening. One woman admitted she thought it was a course to do with hairdressing. Even so, the range and fervour of Mr Diggins' presentation earned him a standing ovation and record bookings.

Now retired and living in a village nearby, he has granted permission for the full transcript of his talk to be published for the first time as part of this celebration of village life.

Mr Diggins remarked: "One or two of my prognostications may have been slightly wide of the mark, but it stands up fairly well to the passage of time. Remember, I said all this several years before the end of the last millennium!"

Talk at Rumoledew Village Hall,
Thursday, September 25th, 1986 (7.30pm)

Good evening, ladies and gentlemen, boys and girls. My name is Pete Diggins – you probably know yours –and I am here to encourage a good old Norfolk habit of looking over your shoulder to see where you've come from.

To say I am fascinated by the past is a bit of an understatement. My mother always said I should have rode shotgun for Boadicea, been a scriptwriter for Tom Paine and gone on a sailing course with Horatio Nelson. But it would be unfair to suggest I am frightened of the future. I maintain that close inspection of our roots –solid Norfolk roots in many cases –provides just the right sort of protection against the slings and arrows lined up to greet us in years to come.

My proud Norfolk connections stretch back over two centuries. I was born in a village where my parents and grandparents on my father's side spent fair parts of their lives. That in itself makes me a bit of a novelty in this fast-changing county although I am fully aware there are people in this audience with similar links.

I agree with country writer Clarence Henry Warren who declared "The best of England is a village" as war clouds piled up in 1940. Perhaps it was more of an elegy than a eulogy but we would be wrong to imagine a murky tide of urban insensitivity waiting to wash away all those rural delights we hold so dear.

Yes, we must beware the rosy haze of nostalgia, although some aspects of the "good old days" do stand up to the harshest scrutiny. For example, there was genuine comfort in knowing everyone in the village... even if that did mean your personal business could slip into the public domain. And it wasn't that long ago when the baker left a nice warm loaf on the lavatory seat in the little shed down the yard!

My father worked on the land. His father and two uncles had worked on the same farm. I went to grammar school and then on to university to study history. A little snapshot, if you like, of the biggest change in Norfolk during the 20th century.

Very few folk here tonight have direct links with agriculture. Very few can appreciate the vital age-old relationship between the village and its working countryside, a relationship that was the reason for the community's existence.

This century has seen the breaking of the village's umbilical tie to the land that gave it birth, roots and reality. Rumoledew, steeped in farming ways, was a self-sufficient community set within its own geographical and social boundaries, largely fending for itself, supplying its own needs and rarely bothering to look outwards

I like to describe places like this as once being an extended family with its own bounded social hierarchy. Isn't it ironic how the individual villager has achieved a form of "liberation" while his neighbours in town and city often seek a return to the reassuringly small community that some villagers were glad to escape!

Tourists

Some of my more cynical colleagues, perched in their academic ivory towers, are claiming we might as well all be tourists today. They say the village is now virtually the antithesis of its own traditions. It's no longer self-sufficient and instead largely depends on town or city for goods, services, jobs, entertainment and maintenance of its infrastructure.

They add, very loudly, that the countryside has simply lost

control of its own affairs and ambitions. In short, it has become the town's toy, a quaint backwater decked out in hemlock and hogweed to act as a romantic backdrop to the stage of urban life.

Fetching language, but I cannot go along with this bleak analysis. Countless jobs on our farms have gone through mechanisation and radical changes in agriculture. But villages will adapt and inspire new forms of employment and so thrive as vibrant alternatives to living and working in places full of traffic, noise and giant office blocks.

Now, it is important for the future of our Norfolk villages that growth is not just imposed from outside, mainly by developers with nothing more subtle than a money-making agenda. A village must have the freedom to grow at its own pace to meet its own needs.

Pressure is mounting on smaller communities to take their share of newcomers being lured to greener pastures. That often means an ugly rash of new housing totally out of character with what's already there. We know the parish council will object but the district council or county council carry more clout if they want to use it. Even if the village is backed to the hilt, appeals by would-be developers to the Department of the Environment can turn guidelines, structure plans and common sense on their head.

Native pride

I'm not always popular for saying this, but the latest gospel of enterprise and prosperity ringing across this area – one of the last great outposts of real civilisation –does not take sufficient heed of native pride. The diehard spirit has to be strongest among those who can make telling comparisons between yes-

terday's rich hedgerows and clear waters and what we have –
or what we are told we should have –today.

True, many locals (me included) can show automatic aversion to change, but we have every right to be at our most
belligerent when alterations look like being imposed on us. A
deep affection for the past – and that is what any historian
worth his salt is about –ought to be used as part of the platform
for Norfolk's future, not mocked as a cobwebbed corner where
old eccentrics suck straw, shake their heads and pitchforks and
mutter strange oaths.

Too many important decisions are being made by people
who have no respect for or knowledge of Norfolk's heritage.
Quite bluntly, they see it no more than an area to be brought
into line, bang up to date. Comparisons cannot hurt them...
because they cannot make them.

Norfolk will continue to change, even out here in the sticks,
but the process has to be more of a natural one. Simple geogra-
phy kept this old county out of the firing line for so long. That
funny bit sticking out into the North Sea like an ample back-
side, almost an island in its own right, went its own sweet way.
Well, that's a luxury now denied by market forces and the "dis-
covery" of an area rich in untapped resources. Isn't it
remarkable how many of those who scoff at the countryside for
its peculiar manners so out of touch with the real world now
want a bit of the action!

I am not a political animal. I prefer to cast a plague on all
their houses when it comes to sensible thinking and treatment
of our more rural areas on the last lap of the 20th century. I do
not want to see even more lovely meadows slide under concrete
because strangers are demanding dormitories. You won't collect
too many votes for saying things like that. It's much too

straightforward, too brutally honest. But wanton destruction has been carried out in so many other places despite all the dire warnings. Ask newcomers to this blessed county why they came here and the vast majority will reply because it is so much better than what they left behind.

Passion for past

So, you'll gather there will be no bias whatsoever in my forthcoming course on cleaning up our village roots! I just want to turn a passion for the past into an integral part of preparations for a lively and satisfying future. I don't want villages to fossilise. I want them to flourish – but not at the behest of greedy outsiders.

Communities like Rumoledew still offer a different assessment of life's priorities. Many of you were lucky enough to be born and raised in a place where fresh air, uplifting views, healthy strolls, family bonds and general togetherness have long been taken for granted. Others were lucky to stumble across Norfolk's answer to Brigadoon – and I hope you are suitably grateful for being allowed to keep it going!

A village like this remains as proof positive that new buildings need not obliterate a landscape but rather find harmony within it. It has survived foreign invasions, the Black Death, serfdom and countless famines. I reckon it should see off a tatty arm of modern speculators.

It may be strange now to think that less than two centuries ago the majority of people in this country were to be found living in villages. And don't forget that the English village is part of the heritage of much more than just England. Many of the folk who settled in the New World, in the United States of America, Canada, Australia, New Zealand and other far-off spots were English villagers.

The ancestors of Abraham Lincoln lived at Swanton Morley, near East Dereham, and three Lincoln brothers moved from Hingham in Norfolk to Hingham in Massachusetts to join their old vicar, Robert Peek, at the new village which he and his neighbours had founded.

I have scoured the pages of several old Norfolk directories to help paint a picture of a Rumoledew world we can still recognise in part. Some family names of the mid-1800s live on proudly in this area although most of the trades have passed into rural history.

The population here in 1891 was 426, apparently fairly close to today's figure, and there were 52 children attending the village school, where Henry George Richards was headmaster. We'll find out in the coming weeks how many of those names from just under a century ago still ring a bell.

Main crops

There were no less than 19 farmers, plus three cow keepers, with wheat, barley and turnips the main crops. James Howling was parish clerk. Charities included the rector's dole of £12 and Buscall's charity of £2 8 shillings for bread to be distributed on certain Sundays. Hands up all those who still get their free loaves!

The church of St Bartholomew was described as being a building of flint with stone dressings in the Gothic style and a lofty embattled western tower with pinnacles and four bells. The stained east window was erected in 1862 by the Rev. Richard Walters, late rector, in memory of his first wife, Emily.

The church register dates back to 1548 and will furnish us with plenty of valuable material. The church tower, by the way, has had something of a chequered career. It was struck by lightning in 1870 and "serious structural faults" were found a few years later.

I am most grateful to those who brought old photographs to this evening's meeting and they will illuminate our path into the past. A couple stand out after early inspection –dressmaker Hannah Everett and cattle dealer Sidney Mortlock.

It appears they were among Rumoledew's most colourful characters of the late Victorian era. I'm reliably informed that Hannah Everett had a strong reputation as "wise woman" of the village, curing warts and other afflictions with the laying on of hands. Sidney Mortlock was also a renowned Methodist preacher of the old fire-and-brimstone brigade.

Sidney Mortlock – cattle dealer
and fiery preacher

Hannah Everett, dressmaker and
"wise woman" of the village.

Hall of Fame

I'm sure there must be many more outstanding personalities from the past waiting to stake a claim for a place in Rumoledew's Hall of Fame. Folk like Myra Vincent, believed to be the first shopkeeper in the village, blacksmith Samuel Peacock, market gardener Thomas Gaze and wheelwright Robert Loads.

Old photographs apart, you can rummage around for things such as family records, school registers and reports, newspaper cuttings, parish council minutes, letters (especially those sent home in wartime), farm sales catalogues, programmes from notable village events (like Coronation sports and church concerts), shopping lists and receipts to show how tastes and prices have changed and, perhaps most precious of all, personal diaries

Who knows, we might be put on our mettle by one of Sidney Mortlock's more fiery sermons, although I understand he tended to preach off the cuff as soon as he got stirred up. Did Hannah Everett leave any written evidence of her curing powers? You'll be surprised at what comes to light before this year is out.

I know there's a strong feeling for the past in this village and most of its immediate neighbours. That's the main reason I am here, to help you tap into even more rich veins of local history and then place all those fresh discoveries at the disposal of natives and newcomers alike.

I do emphasise that this exciting exercise is not confined to those bred and born in the area. Local history does not operate a closed shop. I hope sincerely that new residents will signal their intent to put down useful roots of their own by joining in wherever possible.

Some will have Norfolk connections already, so here's a golden opportunity to dig a bit deeper and see what comes to the surface.

This is really all about local pride, ideally suited to a village of this size, and I can't wait to get cracking.

Let me return to Charles Henry Warren and his inspiring book, England Is a Village, for a clarion call on this September evening in the Norfolk countryside we know and love. At a time of great national strife in 1940, he wrote; "England's might is still in her fields and villages; and though the whole weight of mechanised armies roll over them to crush them, in the end they will triumph.

"The best of England is a village."

A different kind of village and a different kind of battle these days. But the call to arms is just as loud and just as laudable.

22

THE LAST WORD

Alec Paine compiles and edits The Muckspreader, Rumoledew's parish magazine. It has appeared intermittently since the 1950s although publication became far more regular after he took over in 1995. Alec also encouraged current residents to give their views in this volume.

I wasn't born in the village. There we are, a frank admission that I'm the right sort of person to sift through all its yesterdays, size up all its todays and suggest what might be in some of its tomorrows.

After a teaching career of over 30 years in a remote Fenland parish, a growing Cambridgeshire town (see, I have travelled widely) and, finally, a coastal community near Yarmouth, I looked for a small but lively corner of the Norfolk empire to embrace my dotage.

Rumoledew fitted the bill perfectly with enough going on to keep curiosity aroused and creative juices flowing and enough old-fashioned charm and good manners to allow periods of gentle introspection.

One of the big advantages of carrying no emotional baggage into rural retirement is you can take a wider view, weigh up both sides of an argument and give an honest opinion without fear of favouring any traditional local prejudices.

With no axes to grind, no family honour to protect, I had no qualms about taking over The Muckspreader and putting my own stamp on it. It's now in circulation six times a year – it was never more than quarterly before I became editor – and provides a cheerful and challenging platform for village activities, past present and future, as well as for all sorts of views and articles with a humorous flavour.

While I encourage healthy leg-pulling among contributors, I warn strongly against it spilling over into malice. Of course, some people possess a better sense of fun than others, but care has to be taken not to give deliberate offence. Laws of libel and slander apply just as much in small settlement as they do on radio and television and in newspapers.

I have collected all but a few copies of The Muckspreader published since the first edition put together by Dr E G Osborne in 1953, a single sheet dealing mainly with village activities for the Coronation.

It seemed appropriate to select various extracts from the files to complement a series of views put across by current residents. Comparisons can be melodious it appears, as characters and incidents from the past strike telling chords with what's going on today.

Perhaps that's one of the key strengths of village life – continuity. A strong Norfolk fundamentalist streak still runs through Rumoledew, most notably upheld by Mike Boldero, Walter Grimes, Linda Horton and Enid Trett.

They are proud to represent the "old guard" when what they

see as homegrown virtues are under threat, although an acceptance that a more cosmopolitan world can bring some benefits
lifts them out of the worst excesses of the drawbridge brigade.

Younger voices swell into a plaintive chorus for the right to
play a part in the village's future. A blatant lack of affordable
housing in the countryside will force too many of them to leave
an area they still love.

How ironic that previous generations could be tied to
poorly-paid jobs on the land because a family cottage went with
the employment! Now all but a few of those jobs have gone and
those renovated cottages house well-off incomers.

There was no coercion involved in compiling this snapshot
of a Norfolk community striving to come to terms with radical
changes while holding on to a proud and colourful history. It
must be fairly typical of what's happening to similar sized villages across the country.

We are used to dire warnings and even more "far-reaching
reports" about threats to rural pubs, shops and schools through
a lack of low-cost homes. While Rumoledew's facilities remain
intact, with the school thriving, it would be foolhardy to show
any complacency over the future.

Wealthy commuters, the well-heeled retired and peace-
seeking tourists must help the stoic natives to maintain a
reasonable balance, blending best of the old with most benefi-
cial of the new.

What that might involve ought to keep the village going for
a few more centuries.

Now, it's only fair that I should own up to something that
isn't generally known about me after persuading other contributors to this tome to do the same.

Apart from not being born in this village, my Norfolk pedigree is impeccable. Parents and grandparents all proud Bloaters from Yarmouth. Many relatives in and around town, including two aunts who ran boarding houses.

So where did I first see the light of day? Only glorious Felixstowe on the Suffolk coast on a wet Monday morning! My parents were on holiday "abroad" when I decided to arrive several weeks early.

I've been ahead of my time ever since. That's how I discovered the unbridled delights of Rumoledew, a village with a true Norfolk heart.

LOCAL NAMES ON THE WING

Thanks to our dialect champion Mike Boldero for answering the query about local names for birds.

The wood pigeon is known as a dow, the yellowhammer a guler and the bluetit a pickcheese.

Mike also draws attention to the following: barley-bird (nightingale), blood-ulf (bullfinch), caddow (jackdaw), drawwater (goldfinch), dunnock (hedge sparrow), harnser (heron), hornpie (lapwing), mavis (song thrush), spink (chaffinch), thick-knee (Norfolk plover or stone curlew) and woodsprite (woodpecker).

He realises there are many others to add to that list and would be pleased to hear from anyone who can do so.

The Muckspreader, 2003

STRETCHING IT

Overheard at village function: "Trouble with him is he thinks in inches and talks in yards."

The Muckspreader, 1981

HARD TO SEE
The parish council has agreed to have verges cut along Back Lane as hemlock is making it difficult for drivers to see round bends in the road.

The Muckspreader, 1958

ROLL CALL
Overheard in village shop:"I must have one o'them rolls of Anthrax".

The Muckspreader, 1979

TIMELY TONIC
Overheard in The Four Ferrets:"If time is a great healer, we should all be cured by the time we get to see the doctor."

The Muckspreader, 1998

ONION TIPS
Myra Hooper offers this advice on pickling onions.

Select small pickling onions or shallots. Peel carefully without cutting the onion. Wash and cover them with brine, which can be made by mixing sufficient water to cover the onions and two ounces of salt to each pint of water needed. Allow the onions to stand in this brine for 24 hours. Drain them, wash and dry before packing onions into jars. Cover them with cold spiced vinegar and seal the top.

The Muckspreader, 1972

OUR VILLAGE
By Walter Grimes, age 91

When I'm called home to skies above
And leave this place I know and love
I'll take some little bits with me
To go with cockles for my tea
A shoof of corn from harvests done
A shiny horse brass to catch the sun
A hoe and hook and an army coat
Buttoned up right under my throat
A sugar beet nipped up with frost
A favourite bank all green and mossed
Peals of laughter from village lads
Who opened gates and followed dads
Along the rows and on the stacks
To toughen hands and stiffen backs
My fourses bag can take the rest
As daylight dips beyond the west.

The Muckspreader, 2009

Other Books by Keith Skipper from Halsgrove

Normal for Norfolk
Confessions of a Norfolk Squit Merchant
How to Survive in Norfolk
Keith Skipper's Norfolk Quiz Book
Keith Skipper's Norfolk Bedside Book
The Bumper Book of Norfolk Squit